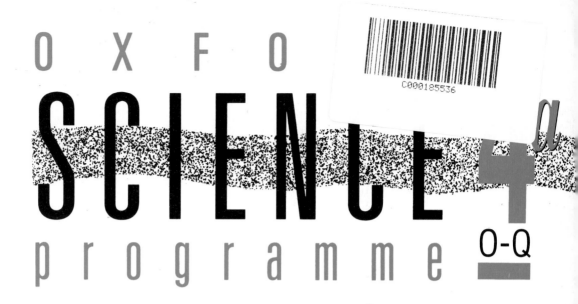

OXFORD SCIENCE programme 4a

O-Q

SCIENCE DEPARTMENT

Consultant Editor: **Paul Denley**

Managing Editor: **Stephen Pople**

Writing Team:

James Bradberry
Stephen Gater
Terry Hudson
Phil Lidstone
David Lossl
Jim Sage
Linda Scott
Stephen Stretch
Susan Williams

Oxford University Press 1992

Oxford University Press
Walton Street
Oxford OX2 6DP

Oxford New York Toronto
Delhi Bombay Calcutta Madras Karachi
Petaling Jaya Singapore Hong Kong Tokyo
Nairobi Dar es Salaam Cape Town
Melbourne Auckland
and associated companies in
Berlin Ibadan

© Stephen Pople, Paul Denley et al 1992

All rights reserved. This publication may not be reproduced, stored or transmitted,
in any forms or by any means, except in accordance with the terms of licences issued
by the Copyright Licensing Agency, or except for fair dealing for the purposes of
research or private study, or criticism or review, as permitted under the Copyright,
Design and Patents Act, 1988.

Enquiries concerning reproduction outside those terms should be addressed to the
Permissions Department, Oxford University Press

Printed in Spain by Gráficas Estella, S.A.

ISBN 0 19 914381 1

O X F O R D
SCIENCE
programme

National Curriculum Key Stage 4

Contents

Module O
The Earth and beyond

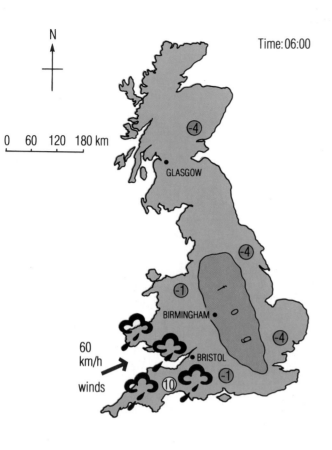

Time: 06:00

burning candle

carbon dioxide gas

Module P
Waves and currents

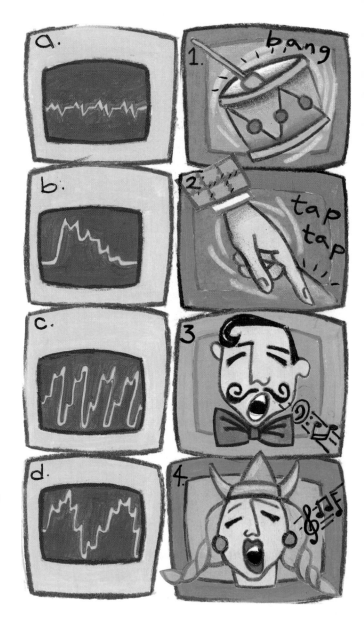

Key

■ Establishing ideas

■ Investigating further

■ Applying new ideas

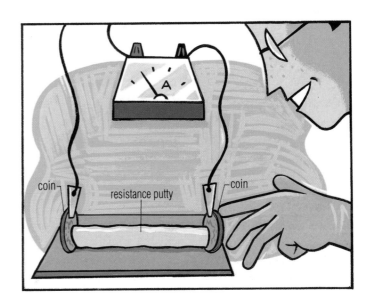

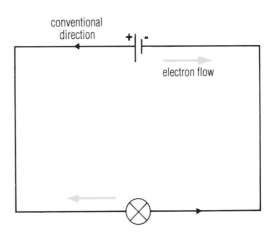

Module Q
Life and health

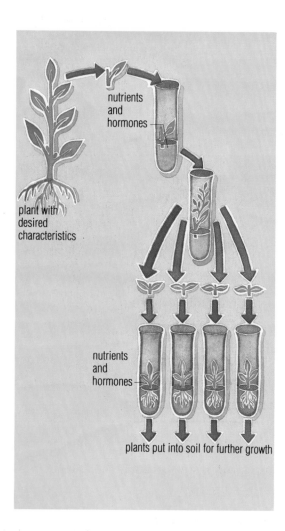

nutrients and hormones

plant with desired characteristics

nutrients and hormones

plants put into soil for further growth

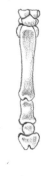

Key

■ Establishing ideas

■ Investigating further

■ Applying new ideas

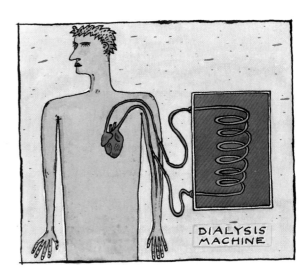

DIALYSIS MACHINE

Introduction

This book forms part of the *Oxford Science Programme*. Its explanations and investigations have been specially designed for Key Stage 4 of the National Curriculum for Science.

The book is divided into three modules, each dealing with a different aspect of science. Each module is made up of double-page spreads. These have been arranged in groups called units. At the start of a unit, you will be asked to discuss and review what you know, including ideas developed in earlier parts of the Programme. Next, you will carry out activities and investigations to extend your understanding. Finally, you will have the chance to apply your knowledge in new contexts. So, working through each unit, the pattern will normally be:

> establishing ideas
> investigating further
> applying new ideas

You may also find that, towards the end of each module, you will be asked to apply ideas which you developed and tested in the earlier units.

Module 0
The Earth and beyond

In the first unit, you start by investigating different types of rocks and their characteristics. Then you consider how rocks are formed and reformed in an endless cycle of change. You examine sedimentary, igneous and metamorphic rocks and the ways in which their properties arise.

In the second unit, you look at how earthquakes and volcanoes have provided clues about the structure of the Earth. You also consider the Earth's great continental plates and the evidence for their movements.

The third unit deals with the weather and some of the factors which influence it, including air pressure, and the huge systems of convection currents that operate in the Earth's atmosphere. You consider what happens when masses of cold and warm air meet and how these can be identified on meteorological maps.

The fourth unit looks at the Earth in relation to the rest of the Solar System. You consider the Sun and its planets in more detail. You examine the way in which satellites and their orbits depend on gravity, and how gravitational pull gives rise to the tides. Finally, you look into the origins of planets, stars, galaxies and the Universe itself.

Module P
Waves and currents

In the first unit, you look at different types of waves, including sound waves, ripples on water, and electromagnetic waves such as light. You explore how waves can be classified and measured, and investigate some of their properties. You also consider the practical uses of waves including cameras, medical treatment, music and communications.

In the second unit, you investigate electrical circuits, voltage and current and how to measure them, and the uses of switches, including logic gates. You discover how some materials conduct current less easily than others and how this means that electrical energy may be changed into heat.

In the third unit, you consider how electricity can be used safely in the home, and how amounts of electrical energy and power can be calculated.

The fourth unit starts by taking a closer look at what electricity is and where it comes from. You find out how 'particles' of electricity are used in TV and X-ray tubes, and how these particles have links with electromagnetic waves.

Module Q
Life and health

Living things, including humans, inherit characteristics from their parents. In the first unit, you investigate the basic principles of genetics to find out how this may happen. You find out how living cells carry coded information, how the secrets of this code were discovered, and how animal and plant breeders, and scientists, put the principles to practical use.

In the second unit, you examine how life may have evolved on Earth, and the evidence which Charles Darwin considered in arriving at his theory of natural selection.

In the third unit, you start by exploring some of the factors which may help or harm people's health. From here, you investigate how scientists' understanding of the human body has improved over the centuries, and some of the important medical advances which have resulted. You also consider how some drugs are used as medicines, while others are harmful.

In the fourth unit, you investigate diseases, how they are caused, how they can be spread, and the methods which scientists have developed for giving protection against some of them.

O   The Earth and beyond

O 1.1 Looking at rocks

Shale · Sandstone · Slate · Schist · Marble · Granite

Investigating Rocks

In the photograph above, you can see a selection of rocks. These are just a small fraction of the many different types of rock found on Earth. In this spread, you will take a closer look at some of these rocks (or ones supplied by your teacher) to see what you can find out about them.

Rocks have many different properties. Some of these are described on the opposite page. With your group, plan and carry out investigations into rock properties. Then decide how you think each sample of rock might have been formed and what might have happened to it in the past.

Things to think about
- Will your group try all the investigations? Or will you divide up the tasks with different groups and then pool your ideas?

What to do
- Decide what properties you will investigate. The information on the opposite page will give you some ideas, and suggest questions that might need answering.
- Plan your investigations.
- Plan any tables you need for recording your results.
- Carry out your investigations.

Properties to investigate

Colour
Does each sample have the same colour throughout? Does the colour vary? Is the colour only on the surface? If so, why do you think this might be?

Hardness
Some rocks are harder than others. Can you think of a way of comparing hardness? Remember: hard rocks are more difficult to scratch, and some rocks break more easily.

Texture
Some rocks are smooth; others are lumpy, or grainy. If there are grains, can you see any more detail using a hand lens? How big is the grain size? Does the texture give you any clues about how the rock might have been formed?

Layering
Are any of the rocks layered? If so, how do you think the layers might have been formed?

Fossils
Some rocks contain fossils (you may need a hand lens to see them). How do you think they got there? Do rocks with fossils have any other features in common?

Porosity
Some rocks are porous. This means that they are full of tiny holes and can absorb water. How could you compare different rocks to find out how porous they are?

Reaction to acids
What happens when acids are dropped on the samples? Do all the samples behave in the same way?

Density
The density of a substance tells you how many grams there are packed into each centimetre cubed. It can be calculated using this equation:

$$\text{density (in g/cm}^3) = \frac{\text{mass (in g)}}{\text{volume (in cm}^3)}$$

Finding the volume is more difficult than finding the mass because rock samples usually have irregular shapes. One way of finding the volume is to put the sample in a measuring cylinder partly filled with water, and then see how much the water level rises on the volume scale:

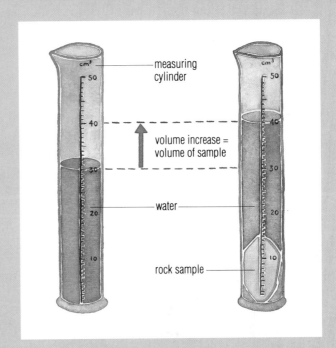

measuring cylinder

volume increase = volume of sample

water

rock sample

When you have finished...

1   With your group, discuss how you think each type of rock might have been formed and what its past history might have been.
2   Look at all the rock samples. By considering similarities and differences, see if you can sort the rocks into groups.
3   Find an interesting way of presenting the results of your investigations and your conclusions, so that others can see them.
4   Compare your results with those from other groups.

Looking at uses

Rocks have many uses, either as construction materials, or as a source of raw materials for industry.

5   Discuss the different samples of rock you have investigated with your group. Decide what practical uses you think these materials might have.
6   Survey your neighbourhood to find the different ways in which rocks are used.
7   Make a poster so that other people can see the results of your discussions and survey.

*O*1.2 *A cycle of change*

The rocks of the Earth are being formed, destroyed and formed again in an endless **cycle** of change. With your group:

1 Decide what you think the term 'cycle' means. Give some examples of cycles.

2 Decide what you think the words in the boxes on the right mean. Use them to draw a flow diagram to show what is meant by the rock cycle.

3 How long do you think it might take for a particle of rock to move through this cycle?

deposition	erosion
weathering	transport

Changes on Rocky Island

Below, you can see a picture of Rocky Island. Very, very slowly, the island is changing shape. New hills are forming as rocks are pushed up by earth movements.

4 Make a list of the different **landforms** (features) on the island. Decide how you think each feature was formed.

The house marked **X** was built 60 years ago. Then, it was more than 20 metres from the cliff.

5 Why is the house at the cliff's edge now? What might happen to it in the future?

6 If you had to recommend two safe sites for housebuilding, which sites would you choose, and why? List the sites you would *not* choose, and why.

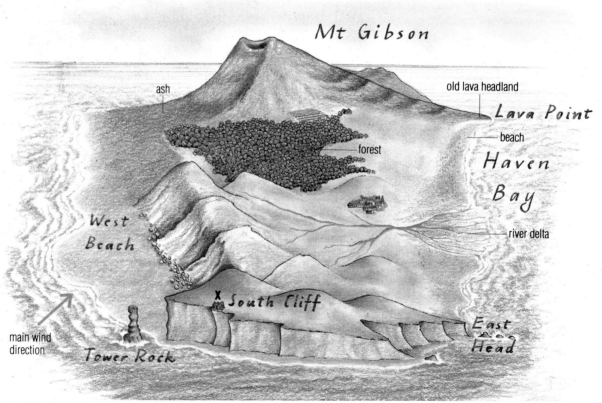

Mt Gibson

ash

old lava headland

Lava Point

beach

forest

Haven Bay

river delta

West Beach

X *South Cliff*

main wind direction

Tower Rock

East Head

Rocky Island

More changes

Photographs **A** and **B** show two places where changes are happening.

7 Describe the changes which are happening in each place. To do this, look for clues which might answer these questions:

- Are there any loose rock fragments? If so, how have they been moved?
- How big are the rock fragments? Are they small (sand), medium (pebbles), or large (boulders)?
- Are new rocks being formed, or old rocks being broken down?

A closer look

When sand and pebbles are moved about, they change shape. Here are some ideas two students had about a beach:

Pebbles and sand from a river bed will be less rounded than pebbles and sand from a beach.

Small pebbles will be more rounded than large ones.

- Compare sand and pebbles from a beach and from a river. See if you can find out how true these statements are.

You need
Hand lens, microscope, sand from a river, sand from a beach, pebbles from a river, pebbles from a beach.

8 What differences did you find between pebbles and sand from a river and those from a beach? How would you explain these differences? Make a chart to present your ideas.

Return to Rocky Island

New rocks are slowly being formed on Rocky Island.

9 Name *two* different ways in which new rocks are being formed.

10 Look at Mount Gibson on Rocky Island. What type of mountain is it? How can you tell?

11 Name *two* rock materials that have come from this mountain. Which of these will produce most beach material?

12 Which coast of the island will be eroding more quickly, the east or the west? Why?

13 Where on the island will new sediments be forming?

O 1.3 Breaking rocks

When rocks become exposed to the weather at the Earth's surface, they start to change. This is called weathering. You can find out more about the effects of weathering by trying these investigations with your group.

Before you start:
- Plan each investigation.
- Make a list of the things you need.
- Decide how you will record your results.

When you have finished:
- Prepare a report on what you found.

Lifetimes of weathering

- Carry out a survey of the gravestones in your local churchyard or cemetery. The readability of the dates will give you a clue about the rate of weathering.

Things to think about:
- Are all the gravestones made of the same type of materials? Are they all exposed to the same type of weather?
- Can you work out a method of grading the amount of weathering of each gravestone?
- Will you include photos in your report?

1 What did your investigation tell you about rates of weathering?
2 Were there any differences between rates of weathering? How would you explain them?

Crumbling rocks

If rocks start to dissolve, this is an example of **chemical weathering**.

3 What rocks might be affected by chemical weathering? (To answer this question, think back to the results of the investigations which you carried out in spread P1.1)

- Design and carry out an investigation to find out how pieces of limestone are affected by these kinds of water:
  distilled water
  tap water
  rainwater
  water with hydrochloric acid added

Useful information
- Different kinds of water can have different acidities. The strength of acids is measured on the pH scale. pH 1 is the strongest acid. pH 7 is neutral. You can measure the pH of water using universal indicator paper.

Things to think about
- Will you measure the pH numbers of the different types of water?
- Do you expect rainwater to be slightly acid?
- Do you think the size of the rock pieces might affect the result of the test?

4 What did you conclude from your investigation? Do you think that limestone might be chemically weathered by the action of rainwater?

The action of ice

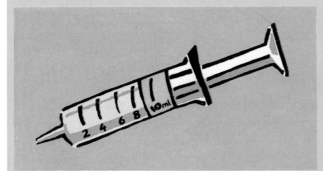

- Find out what happens when some water is frozen in a syringe.
- Find out what happens when an old, glass bottle filled with water is left in a freezer overnight. *Safety: the bottle must be sealed inside a plastic bag and examined with great care.*

5 What happened to the syringe?
6 What happened to the bottle? Can you explain why?
7 Some rocks have tiny cracks in them which soak up rainwater. What do you think will happen if the rainwater freezes?

After the weathering

Erosion is the movement of loose material. Once a rock has been weathered, its surface is more easily eroded .

9 In how many different ways is erosion happening on the island shown below?
10 In the photograph at the bottom of the opposite page, why do you think the rocks are such a strange shape ?

Cracking rocks

Some students decided to investigate whether different rocks would be cracked by very cold weather. But they had different ideas about how to carry out the tests. You can see these above.

- With your group, decide what method you would use. Then carry out the investigation yourself.

8 Compare your results with other groups. Which method was most effective in cracking the rocks? Why?

O 1.4 Making rocks

As ice, wind, rivers and sea waves erode the land, they loosen broken rocks which become boulders, pebbles, sand and mud. When these settle, they are called **sediments**.

1 Why do you think some rocks are called sedimentary rocks?

Look back at the picture of Rocky Island on spread O1.2.

2 Where are new sediments being formed?
3 What landforms are being worn down to provide the new material?

Forming sediments

■ Find out what happens when equal amounts of sand, gravel and clay are shaken in a jar with water and then left.
■ Draw and explain your results.

Useful information
• Use at least four times as much water as the materials you mix in. Leave space at the top of the jar for mixing during shaking.

The diagram below shows a section (side) view of part of Rocky Island.

4 Can you decide where it is on the island?
5 The following labels have been left off the diagram. Where should each one go?

Labels:

   mud (forms shale)
   sand (forms sandstone)
   pebbles (form conglomerate)

Make your own rocks!

■ Try making your own 'rocks' by pressing damp sand into a plastic cup.
■ Turn this out onto a sheet of paper. Does the sand stay together? If so, why?
■ What happens when the sand dries out?
■ Now try mixing damp sand with other materials. The diagram below shows you some possibilities. Keep your artificial rocks so that you can test them later.
■ Now try making some rocks using gravel (or pebbles) mixed with the sand.

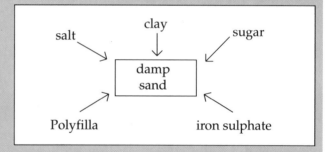

Testing your rocks

■ When your artificial rocks are dry, test them to find out which is the hardest.
■ What was the effect of adding different substances to damp sand and gravel? Draw a chart to show what you found (leave room on your chart for the results of the next tests).
■ Plan and carry out some tests to find out how your new rocks are affected by weathering, such as exposure to water or frost.
■ Add these results to your chart.

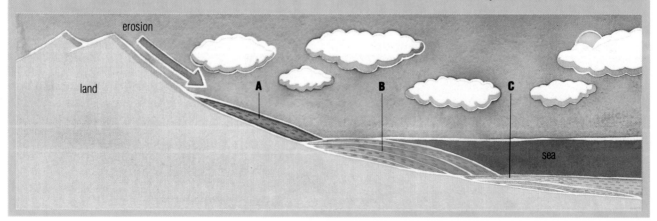

Sloppy to solid

The rock fragments in sediment are called **grains**. They can range from mud (very fine particles) to pebbles and boulders.

On the sea bed, sediment is squeezed by the weight of new layers forming above. This process is called **compaction**. It can take millions of years. Dissolved substances may cement the grains together to make new rock which is hard and solid. This process is called **cementation**.

- Compare the hardness and appearance of your artificial rocks with samples of sandstone, conglomerate and shale.
- See if you can decide which of these real rocks was formed from pebbles, which from sand and which from mud.

The diagram on the right shows some layers of sediment on the sea bed.
6 Draw another diagram to show how you think these layers might look after compaction and cementation.

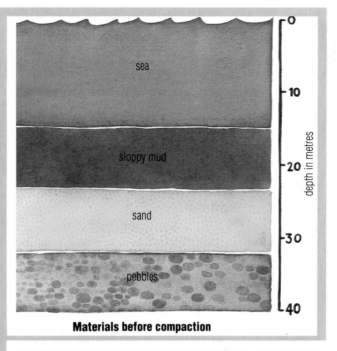

Materials before compaction

More sedimentary rocks

The photograph above shows a cliff. It is a very long time since these layers were sloppy sand and mud on the sea bed. They have been raised up by earth movements.
7 Make a sketch of the photograph and mark in
- where erosion is happening now.
- where deposition is happening now.

The photograph above shows some marks on a piece of sandstone from a cliff.
8 Where on Rocky Island might you find marks like this being formed today?
9 Was the rock in the photograph deposited in deep or shallow water? Give your reasons.
10 What evidence is there that the rock layer was soft when it was deposited?
11 How long do you think it would take for the rock layers that were once below the sea floor to be raised by earth movements: thousands of years or millions of years?

O 1.5 Looking at igneous rocks

Some of the rocks on Rocky Island have formed from volcanic ash and lava. They are examples of **igneous** rocks. Igneous rocks come from **magma**, a molten (melted) material from under the Earth. Magma can erupt at the surface as lava, and cool quickly. Or it can cool very slowly deep underground. When magma cools and solidifies, it forms rock which is made up of tiny crystals.

Look back at the picture of Rocky Island on spread O1.2.
 1 Where are the igneous rocks on the island?
 2 What kind of landforms have they produced?

Here are some investigations to find out more about igneous rocks and their formation.

Cooling into crystals

Igneous rocks are made up of tiny crystals.
 ■ Use a hand lens to look at samples of these igneous rocks: *granite, dolerite, basalt*.
 ■ Compare the crystal sizes and record your findings.

Scientists think that the size of the crystals formed depends on how fast the material cools.
 ■ Test this idea by allowing samples of warm, melted salol to cool and solidify. The diagrams show you how to melt the salol, and put it on a glass slide to cool.

Things to think about
 • How will you make sure that different samples of salol cool at different rates?
 • How will you study the crystal sizes?

Now answer these questions:
 3 What did you discover from your investigation? Does the crystal size depend on whether the salol cools quickly or slowly? If so, how?
 4 How quickly do you think magma must have cooled to form these three rocks: *granite, dolerite, basalt*?
 5 For each of these rocks, decide whether you think it formed by cooling above ground or below ground. Give your reasons.

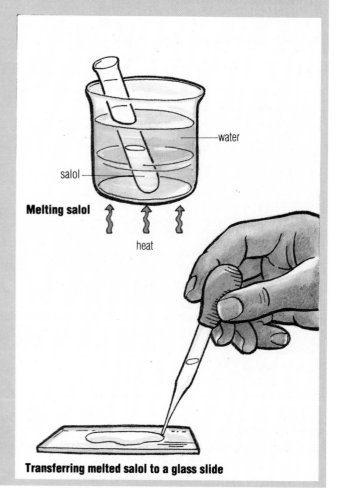

Melting salol

water

salol

heat

Transferring melted salol to a glass slide

Rock types compared

Study samples of these igneous and sedimentary rocks: *granite, basalt, dolerite, sandstone, limestone, shale.*

- Decide which of these are igneous rocks and which are sedimentary.
- Compare the hardness and the grain sizes of the igneous rocks and the sedimentary rocks. You may be able to use results from the investigations in spread O1.1.
- Make a table to show your findings.

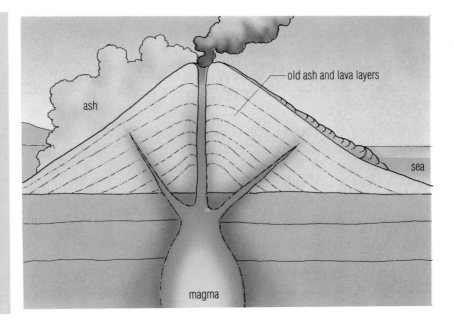

Where did they cool?

The diagram at the top of the page shows a section through a volcano.

6 Sketch your own copy of this section.

7 Add labels to show where you think the following rocks might form after cooling: *basalt, dolerite.*

The photograph on the right shows an igneous rock called **porphyry**. Answer the following with your group.

8 How would you describe the crystal sizes of porphyry?

9 If possible, look at a sample of porphyry, along with granite and basalt. How do the crystal sizes compare?

10 How would you explain the crystal sizes of porphyry? What do you think the 'cooling history' of this rock might have been?

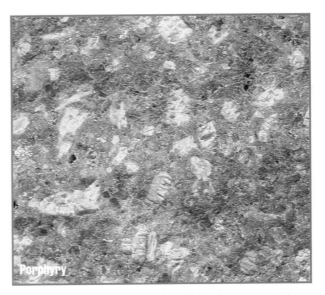

Looking at tuff

Tuff is a type of rock formed from volcanic ash. You can see a photograph of some tuff on the right.

11 If possible, take a close look at a sample of tuff. How do you think the tuff might have been formed?

12 Someone describes tuff as 'sedimentary igneous rock'. What do you think of this as a description? Discuss your ideas with your group.

13 On the sketch of the volcano which you drew before, show where you think that tuff might now be forming.

23

O 1.6 Made from magma

Change happens very slowly in the rock cycle. But once igneous rocks become exposed at the surface, they begin to be worn away. This can produce some interesting landforms.

Volcano views

Some students went to see the volcano on Rocky Island. They were surprised to find people living and working on its slopes. So they asked the local people about their lives. You can see some of their replies above.

Answer these with your group:
1 Give at least one reason for people living and working on the slopes.
2 How is the soil being formed?
3 New soil forms on top of new ash and lava at the rate of 1 cm thickness every 100 years. When were ash and lava last erupted in this area?
4 How do the farmers stop soil erosion?
5 If there are no more eruptions and the volcano becomes extinct, what will eventually happen to this landform?

Exploding volcano

Before it erupted, Mount St Helens in the USA was a mountain with ice and snow at its summit. Then in 1980, one whole side of the mountain exploded, flattening trees over 20 km away.

Eruption of Mount St Helens, 1980

In the photograph of Mount St Helens:

6 What is being erupted from the volcano?

7 Are there any clues which suggest that the mountain is eroding?

During the eruption, huge flows of fluid mud rushed down the mountainside.

8 Where would the water come from?

9 What would be the source of the fine material for the mud?

Lava landform

The Giant's Causeway, County Antrim

Thick layers of new lava shrink slightly as they cool. This causes the rock to form vertical cracks called joints which split the rock into the polygon shapes. You can see some of these in the photograph above.

10 How will water work its way into the rock?

11 What effects will the water have?

12 What has caused the rocks to erode?

Intrusions

Sometimes, magma will cool underground before it can reach the surface. For example, a thin sheet of magma may squeeze its way between the rock layers, where it cools. This is called an **intrusion**.

13 Look back at the diagram of the Rocky Island Volcano on the last spread, O1.5. See if you can find two intrusions in the diagram.

Hard and soft

The diagram above shows a section of land with an intrusion of hard dolerite in softer shale. A river is crossing the land.

14 What do you think will happen as the river erodes the shale? What effect will the intrusion of harder rock have?

15 What landform do you think will be caused by the band of rock on the river bed?

16 Draw an 'after' diagram to summarize the main changes which you think will happen.

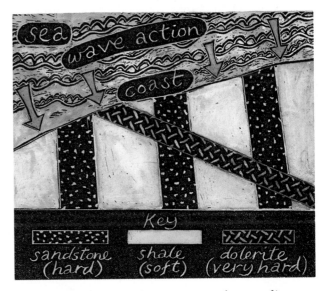

The diagram above shows a map of a coastline. There are hard and soft areas of rock, and an igneous intrusion of dolerite.

17 Draw an 'after' diagram of this situation, to show how you think the coastline will change as a result of erosion by the waves.

O 1.7 Folds and faults

Rock layers can be folded by immense sideways stresses from movements deep below ground. If you place two books either end of a flat teacloth, and then slide them together, you will see that some of the folds get pushed upwards, just as rock layers do when they form **fold mountains**. Look at the photograph on the right.

1 What clue is there that the rocks here are sedimentary?

2 Is there any evidence that you are looking at fold mountains?

3 The rock layers near the mountain peaks contain fossil shells of oysters from 15 million years ago. How do you think they got there?

Modelling folds

When sedimentary layers are folding they stay solid but bend. The downfolds are called **synclines** and the upfolds are called **anticlines.** You can model them using Plasticine.

- Make the model layers as in the diagrams.
- How would erosion affect the layers?
- Sketch the pattern of the layers that you see when you slice through the top of an anticline and a syncline.

Modelling faults

Sometimes, rock layers will break along lines called **faults**. You can model how this happens as well.

- Cut a piece of thin card as below.
- Push on the card as shown and sketch what happens. Mark in the fold and the faults.

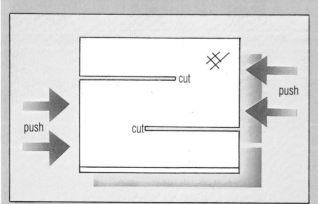

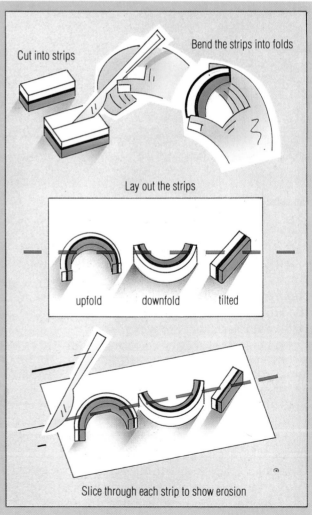

Cut into strips

Bend the strips into folds

Lay out the strips

upfold   downfold   tilted

Slice through each strip to show erosion

The effect of heat

Different rock layers have different strengths. Some layers are **plastic**: this means that they are flexible and will bend into folds. Other layers will snap and break along faults. Rock layers are rather like toffee or Plasticine. The way they react to stress depends on how hot they are.

4 What is the difference between toffee when it is cold and when it is warm? How would you explain the difference?

5 How do you think heat might affect whether a rock layer bends or breaks?

Now try testing some warm and cold Plasticine.

■ Plan and carry out some tests to compare the behaviour of cold and warm strips of Plasticine when these are put under sideways stress.

■ Record your results. Prepare a report which explains what happened.

You need
Strips of hand-warm Plasticine and Plasticine which has come straight from a freezer, items chosen by you.

6 How do you think heat might affect the way rocks deep underground react to stress? Do you think the rocks will fold or fault?

Types of fault

There are three main ways in which rocks can fault. You can see these illustrated in the diagrams on the right.

7 Study the diagrams. Describe how the three types of fault are different.

8 Draw your own copies of the diagrams. Put in arrows to show how the rocks have moved either side of each fault.

9 What type of fault is shown in the fault model on the opposite page?

Looking for evidence

The photograph on the right was taken at Lulworth Cove in Dorset.

10 Describe all the clues that indicate any evidence of earth movement. Give any information you can about the types of folding or faulting you can see, and the direction of movement of the rocks.

11 What do you think might have broken up the face of the cliff?

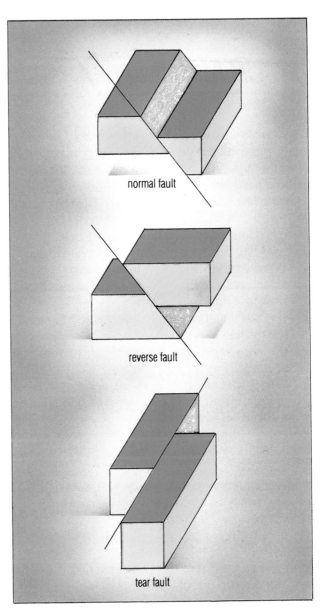

normal fault

reverse fault

tear fault

Types of fault

27

O *1.8 Metamorphic rocks*

Rocks which are normally brittle can fold more easily at depth. But other changes may take place as well. The heat and pressure can be so strong that the particles in buried rocks form new crystals. The changes happen when the rock is still solid: there is no melting. The process of change is known as **metamorphism**. Rocks changed like this are called **metamorphic** rocks.

1 What would you expect to happen to structures like ripple marks or fossils in the rock layers during metamorphism?
2 Look at the photograph on the right. Sketch the outline of the fossil to show how you think it would have looked before it went out of shape.
3 What clues are there to the directions of the forces on the rock? Use your sketch to label the force directions.

Before and after

In metamorphism, sedimentary rocks become new metamorphic ones. Look at some samples to see what changes you can detect.

You need
Steel point, lens, samples of limestone, shale, sandstone, metaquartzite, marble, slate.

What to do
■ Pair up the samples so that you have the correct sedimentary rock and metamorphic rock in each pair.
■ Explain why you paired them as you did.
■ Make a table to record the differences and similarities between each pair of rocks.

Three of the rocks you may have been looking at are shown in the photographs on the right.

4 What happens to the sand grains in sandstone as a result of metamorphism?

People have been using metamorphic rocks like slate and marble for hundreds of years. Other useful materials from metamorphic rocks include diamonds and talc.

5 Find out more about the uses of diamond, talc, slate and marble.

Sandstone

Metaquartzite

Slate

Hot intrusion

The section diagram on the right shows a hot intrusion between some other rocks.

6 Draw your own copy of this diagram. Shade in an area where you think metamorphic rocks will be forming.
7 Why do you think metamorphic rocks will form in this area?
8 Name two types of metamorphic rocks you would expect to find within the metamorphic area.
9 Say what each of these rocks was before it was metamorphosed.
10 On your copy of the diagram, label the areas of igneous, sedimentary and metamorphic rocks.

More metamorphism

The photograph on the right shows examples of schist and gneiss. These are metamorphic rocks which form in conditions of very high pressure and temperature:

11 Describe what each rock is like.
12 Look at the pictures below. Describe what you think they are showing.
13 At what depths are gneiss and schist being formed?
14 Why are the rocks being formed at these depths and not closer to the surface?
15 Why, in some areas, is it possible to pick up samples of gneiss and schist lying on the surface?

Now look at the picture of Rocky Island in spread O1.2.

16 Where on the island would you expect metamorphic rocks to be forming, and why?

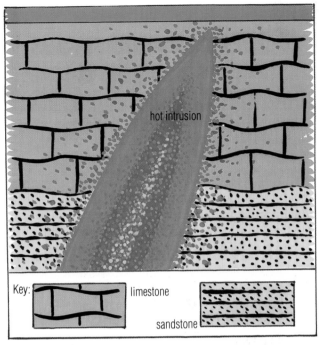

hot intrusion

Key: limestone   sandstone

Schist

Gneiss

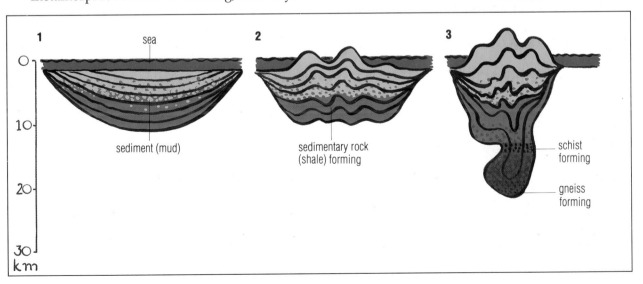

1 sea

sediment (mud)

2 sedimentary rock (shale) forming

3 schist forming

gneiss forming

$\mathcal{O}$ 1.9 Rocks and cycles

Rocks can be eroded, buried as sediment, metamorphosed and uplifted by earth movements. But they are never destroyed, only altered in an endless cycle of change. A single cycle can take many millions of years.

The diagram below shows the main changes which can happen in the **rock cycle.**

1 Decide which of the these labels goes with each of the letters **A** to **G** in the diagram:

> *folding and uplift* *heat and pressure*
> *eruption* *deposition*
> *melting* *erosion and transport*
> *cooling*

2 Describe all the things that might happen to a quartz crystal. Start when it is eroded from an intrusion. Follow it until it becomes part of some molten magma again.

Temperature and depth

Depth beneath Earth's surface in km	Temperature in °C
1	50
2	80
4	140
6	200
8	260

The table above shows the readings taken from a borehole drilled deep in the ground. It shows the temperature at various depths:

3 Use these figures to draw a graph showing how temperature changes with depth.

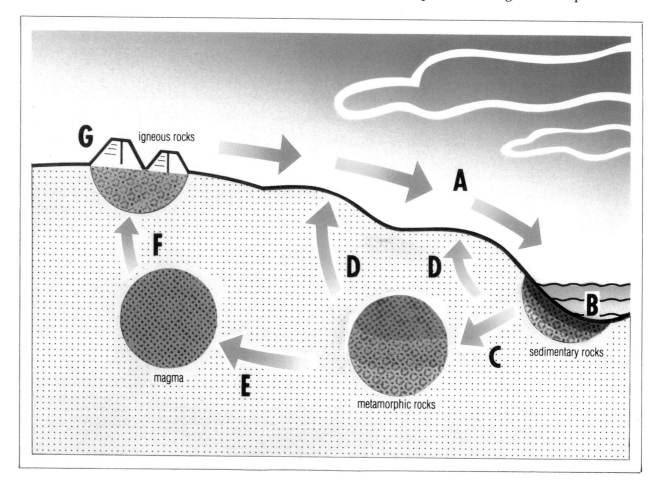

4 What is the temperature increase for each kilometre of depth? Estimate what the temperature might be at a depth of 10 km.

5 What would the temperature be at the depth gneiss might form? (To answer this, you will need information from the previous spread.)

6 Why are rocks more likely to fold than fault at this depth?

7 Rocks normally melt at 1000 °C. At what depth would this temperature be reached?

8 In fact most rocks at this depth remain solid. What does this tell you about the effect of pressure on the melting point of rock?

Local rocks

- If possible, visit a site where rocks are exposed. However, avoid dangerous places like quarries or overhanging cliffs.
- Collect samples of different rocks.
- See if you can identify whether the rocks are igneous, sedimentary or metamorphic.
- Record any evidence of weathering.
- Make a chart to show all your findings.

9 Below, you can see how some students described the rock samples they had found.

10 Decide what each type of rock is and where it would fit on the rock cycle diagram.

A *It is a soft, flaky, dark grey rock.*

B *It is full of large crystals of different colours. Some are black speckles.*

C *It is a light grey, layered rock with fossils, and it fizzes with dilute acid.*

D *This dark grey rock is very hard but splits easily into thin slabs.*

Cliff face

The section diagram below shows a cliff face on Rocky Island. Different types of rock have been labelled **a**, **b**, **c**, **d**, **e**, **f** and **g**. There are three special features **X**, **Y** and **Z**.

11 Which rock do you think is the oldest? Why?

12 Which rock do you think is the youngest? Why?

13 What are the features at **X**, **Y** and **Z** called?

14 Put the following events into the order in which you think they would have happened:
  A intrusion of igneous rock
  B deposition of layered sediments **f** and **g**
  C deposition of layered sediments **a** to **e**
  D folding and uplift

Time capsule

On Rocky Island, all the processes of the rock cycle are acting to change the land. Even its shape will not stay the same. Bearing this in mind, you have to hide a time capsule of the 1990s on the island. It must be somewhere safe where it can still be found in a thousand years time.

15 Study the picture of Rocky Island in spread O1.2. Then decide on the best site for the capsule, giving your reasons.

16 Redraw the picture of the island, as you think it might look a thousand years in the future. Remember to show where the time capsule is.

O 2.1 Inside the Earth

Scientists know that it is nearly 6400 km to the Earth's centre. No one has ever seen rocks from greater depths than the rocks in volcanoes. But, on this page, you may find some clues about conditions inside the Earth.

Molten rock from a volcano

Sharon is a keen caver. She likes caving at all times of the year, though is careful to avoid those periods when there is a risk of flooding.

> I especially like caving in the winter because it feels warmer underground. The temperature stays at around 14°C all the year round.

Harriet is a research scientist who studies volcanoes.

> Molten rock from a volcano can travel up from depths of over 100 kilometres. One of my tasks is to measure its temperature accurately, though it is possible to produce a rough estimate from the colour of the glow.

Anton works in a goldmine in Southern Africa. At a depth of more than 3 kilometres, it is one of the deepest mines in the world.

> Conditions in the mine are hot and uncomfortable. The rocks can reach temperatures of more than 50°C, so cold air has to be blown down to us or we would never survive. Another problem we have is the threat of rock bursts into our tunnels because of the high pressure.

1 What does the information on this page tell you about the inside of the Earth? Decide on the main clues with your group and summarize your findings.
2 Use the table on the right to estimate the temperature of the molten rock in the photograph at the top of the page. How does the temperature compare with a toaster element and a light bulb filament?

Colour of glow	Temperature in °C
red	500 - 900
yellow	900 - 1150
white	above 1150

Looking into density

The density of a rock tells you the number of grams packed into every centimetre cubed. Scientists have worked out that the average density of the whole Earth is 5.5 g/cm^3.

The table on the right shows measurements which were made on some rock samples. All the samples came from near the Earth's surface.

3 Calculate the density of each sample. (It might help to look back to spread O1.1.)

4 If all the samples could be fitted together into a single, solid block, what would its average density be? How does this compare with the Earth's average density?

Scientists think that there may be iron inside the Earth.

■ Measure the density of a sample of iron. Find out how it compares with the average density of the Earth.

Now discuss and answer the following with your group:

5 Do your results support the scientists' idea that there could be iron inside the Earth? If so, why?

6 Do your results *prove* that there is iron inside the Earth? Explain your answer.

7 If there is iron in the Earth, where do your results suggest it might be?

The picture on the right shows one idea which a student had for a model of the Earth: a large ball bearing with Plasticine around it.

■ Measure the density of Plasticine.

■ Measure the density of the steel used in a large ball bearing.

■ Make a model Earth like the one in the diagram and measure its average density.

■ See if you can modify your model so that its average density is exactly the same as that of the Earth.

Section through the Earth

Some students were planning a poster showing a slice through the Earth. They had ideas for labels but weren't sure which ones were correct. You can see their ideas on the right.

9 Decide which labels you think the students should use and where these should be positioned. Then produce your own diagram, with labels added, showing a slice through the Earth.

Rock	Mass in g	Volume in cm^3
sandstone	140.0	50.0
limestone	164.7	61.0
shale	137.2	49.0
granite	182.7	63.0
basalt	153.6	48.0

Did you know?

The gravitational pull of a planet depends partly on its mass. Scientists can use this idea to calculate the mass of the Earth.

8 If scientists know the mass of the Earth, what other information do they need to calculate the average density? How do you think they find this information?

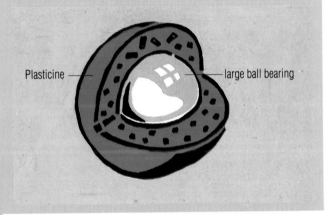

Plasticine —— ——large ball bearing

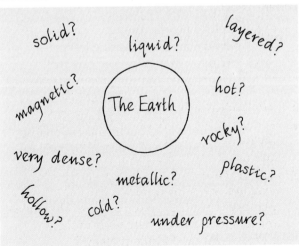

solid? liquid? layered? magnetic? hot? The Earth rocky? very dense? plastic? metallic? hollow? cold? under pressure?

2.2 Vibrations and 'quakes

Detecting vibrations

Don lives in a village. Every time a heavy lorry goes by, the whole house shakes. The council won't do anything unless they have evidence, so he needs to measure the vibrations. But he can't think of the best way to do it.

■ With your group, see if you can solve the problem. You could test your ideas by hitting a solid bench harder and harder with a swinging sand bag. You will need a way of detecting the amount of shudder. The picture on the right may give you some ideas.

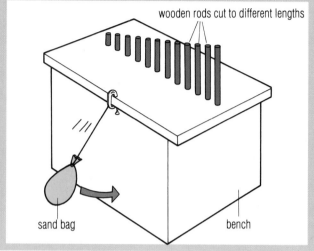

The Earth shudders when there are earthquakes. The travelling vibrations are called **shock waves** or **seismic waves**.

In 1902, G. Mercalli devised a scale for measuring the destructiveness of earthquakes. There is a modern version of his twelve-point scale below.

1 Think of the strongest shudder you produced in your tests. Estimate its number on the Mercalli scale.

A **seismometer** is an instrument used for measuring vibrations from earthquakes. It can detect shock waves even when they have been weakened by travelling hundreds or even thousands of kilometres. The recording it makes is called a **seismogram**.

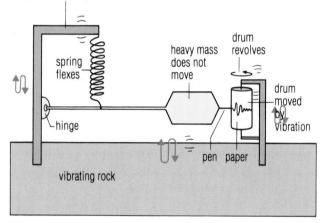

One type of seismometer

Number	Effects of earthquake
1	Not noticed by people
2	Felt by people resting
3	Vibrations like a passing lorry
4	Windows rattle, parked cars rock
5	Doors open and shut, sleepers wake up
6	Felt by everyone, difficult to walk
7	Difficult to stand, bells ring
8	Ground cracks, some houses collapse
9	Pipes burst, much structural damage
10	Most buildings destroyed, dams break
11	Roads and railways break up
12	Total destruction and many deaths

The Mercalli scale

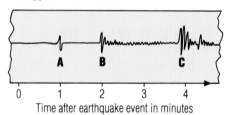

Seismogram (trace from a seismometer)

Look at the diagram of the seismometer.
2 Describe how you think the instrument works.

Look at the diagram of the seismogram. Three pulses of waves were recorded.
3 Which pulse had the highest speed?
4 Which pulse was the slowest?
5 Which pulse had the largest vibrations?

34

Earthquakes in California

The earthquake described on the right was caused by a jerky movement of rocks along the San Andreas fault. A fault happens when two sections of the Earth's upper layer slide past each other. Along the San Andreas fault, there is an average rate of sliding of 5 cm every year. But some sections of rock become locked together rather like the two sides of a zip and may spend many years without moving at all. During this time, stresses build up. Eventually, they are too strong to resist, and the sections move past each other in jerks.

6 Why had people been expecting an earthquake to happen for some time?

7 If the earthquake had happened three hours later, would it have been more disastrous or less? Give your reasons.

8 What was the main cause of death in the earthquake?

9 How did Don Sharp first notice the earthquake?

10 Estimate the level of the earthquake on the Mercalli scale.

11 San Franciscans are still waiting for 'the big one'. When was their last big earthquake?

12 Estimate how many metres of movement might occur if another big earthquake were to happen today.

Study the map of the area with your group.

13 Which do you think are the most dangerous sections of the fault, where really big earthquakes are most likely?

14 Which do you think are the least dangerous sections of the fault?

15 Should San Francisco and Los Angeles have been built where they are? If not, where would you have built two large cities?

16 Draw a poster-size diagram to show your findings. Compare them with other groups.

Did you know?

Scientists now use the **Richter scale** for measuring the magnitude of earthquakes. This scale is based on the total energy released by the earthquake, rather than on its destructiveness. A major earthquake would be 8 or 9 on the Richter scale. But the deeper the source, the less destruction there is likely to be on the surface.

THE DAY THAT TIME RAN OUT

18 October 1989

Few people remember the last time there was an earthquake in San Francisco, back in 1906, but everyone knew that one day the earth would move again. The earthquake struck 50 km south of San Francisco at Santa Cruz.

Last night 280 people died when a highway bridge came crashing down. Many people were crushed in their cars. The earthquake struck suddenly at 5.04 p.m. in the evening rush hour.

Leroy Fitzgerald who works nearby said: 'You could hear it crunching down. Then people were screaming - after about a minute there was just complete silence!'

Don Sharp was on the bridge: 'My car began to shudder. Then I watched cars behind me and in front just vanish. They must have plunged into the water!'

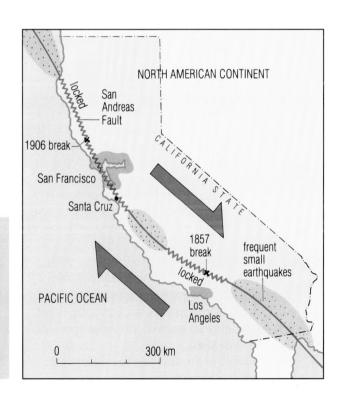

2.3 Earthquake waves

In an earthquake, the sudden rock movements send out vibrations in the form of shock waves. There are three types of waves.

P waves

P waves are 'push and pull' waves: the rock is first compressed and then stretched as each wave passes through. P waves can travel through solids and liquids, deep in the Earth. When they reach the surface, they make the ground shudder up and down. Near the surface, their speed is about 8 kilometres per second.

S waves

S waves are 'shake' waves: the rocks shudder from side to side as they pass. S waves travel at about half the speed of P waves. They can travel deep in the Earth, but cannot pass through liquids (such as molten rock).

L waves

L waves produce a rolling motion rather like waves at sea. They can only travel through surface rocks. Their speed is half that of S waves. But, in an earthquake, they are the most destructive waves of all. Huge fissures (open cracks) can appear on the crests, and close seconds later when the crests become troughs. People, cars and even buildings may be swallowed up.

1 If possible, use a Slinky spring to study the motion of P and S waves. Your teacher will explain how to use the spring, or you can find details in Module P, spread P1.4. Describe how the coils move as the different types of wave pass along the spring.

2 Although P, S and L waves have different motions, a seismometer detects them all with an up-and-down pointer movement. Look at the pulses A, B and C in the seismogram in spread O2.2. Which are the P waves, which the S waves and which the L waves? Why?

3 Imagine that you are in a room when an earthquake happens nearby. Describe what you experience as each of the three types of shock waves pass.

4 Make a table to summarize the differences between the three types of shock waves.

THE EFFECT OF P WAVES

THE EFFECT OF S WAVES

THE EFFECT OF L WAVES

Waves inside the Earth

By studying P and S waves, scientists can find out what the Earth is like deep inside. P and S waves travel faster through denser rocks. At a depth of 3000 km, P waves have a speed of nearly 14 kilometres per second.

5 Are rocks deep in the Earth more dense or less dense than those near the surface? What evidence can you find for your answer on this and the opposite page?

6 L waves give scientists no clues about conditions deep in the Earth. Why not?

When rocks suddenly move and create an earthquake, the centre of the disturbance is called the **focus**. The point on the Earth's surface immediately above is called the **epicentre**. Shock waves travel out from the focus. Using seismometers, scientists can detect the waves at different points around the Earth.

The top diagram on the right shows how scientists think that P and S waves would travel if there were only gradual changes of density within the Earth. In fact, from their seisometer readings, scientists think that the pathways are more like those in the second diagram. There is a **shadow zone** where no P and S waves are detected.

7 The material around the Earth's centre seems to stop S waves passing through. From what you know about S waves, what do you think this material could be like?

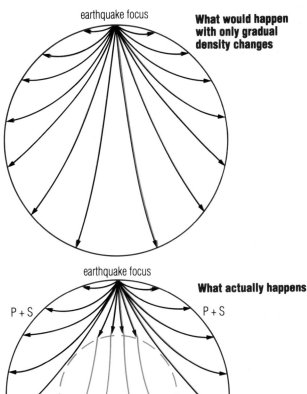

What would happen with only gradual density changes

earthquake focus

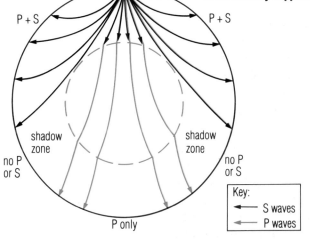

What actually happens

earthquake focus

P + S   P + S

shadow zone   shadow zone

no P or S   no P or S

P only

Key:
⟵ S waves
⟵ P waves

Shadow zone model

Some students decided to make a model to show how shock waves travel through the Earth. They did this by shining light through a beaker of water placed on a white card disc. But they had a problem. They couldn't work out which type of shock waves they were modelling. See if you can decide for them.

- Carry out the experiment. Draw in the shadow patterns and label any shadow zones.
- In your model, what do the card and the beaker of water represent?
- Why does the water create shadow zones?
- Do you think the light rays represent P waves, S waves or L waves?

8 Someone claims that the Earth has a dense liquid core. Is this a reasonable idea? What evidence is there to support it?

The students' model

37

O 2.4 Layers of the Earth

From their studies of P and S waves, scientists think that the Earth has a layered structure. The thin outer surface layer is called the **crust**. Beneath it is the **mantle**, followed by the **outer core** and then the **inner core**.

Below, there is some information about the Earth's layers. With your group.

1   See if you can decide which layer each box refers to.
2   Calculate the radius of the Earth from the average thickness figures given in the boxes. You can assume that the crust is 20 km thick on average.
3   Using the information in the boxes, draw a large, circular, poster-sized diagram of a section through the Earth. It should show the layers to scale. The list of *Things to think about* below might help.

This meteorite is rich in iron and nickel. Scientists think that it may be a fragment from the core of a planet which broke up.

A		
	State:	liquid
	Composition:	mainly iron
	Thickness	2030 km
	Density:	10 - 12 g/cm^3
	Pressure:	very high
	Temperature:	up to 4000 °C

C		
	State:	plastic (flexible) solid
	Composition:	rock
	Thickness	2880 km
	Density:	3.3 - 5.6 g/cm^3
	Pressure:	high
	Temperature:	up to 3700°C

CRUST

MANTLE

OUTER CORE

INNER CORE

B		
	State:	brittle solid
	Composition:	rock
	Thickness	8 km (under oceans) 35 km (continents)
	Density:	2.7 - 2.9 g/cm^3
	Pressure:	low - medium
	Temperature:	250°C (average)

D		
	State:	solid
	Composition:	mainly iron
	Thickness	1440 km
	Density:	over 15 g/cm^3
	Pressure:	very high
	Temperature:	up to 4500°C

Things to think about:
- What scale will you use for your diagram?
- How can you show the thin crust of the Earth to scale?
- Will you use colours and shading in your diagram? If so, what will they represent?

Did you know?

Some hot materials which would normally be molten stay solid at very high pressures. Scientists think that this may be why the Earth has a solid inner core.

True or False?

With your group, look at the statements on the right.

4 Decide which statements you agree with. There are some clues to help you in this spread, but you may also need information from other sources.

The Earth's crust

The Earth has two distinct kinds of crust. **Continental crust** is made of granite and related rocks, together with sedimentary layers. Most of the world's continental land areas are formed from this type of crust. **Oceanic crust** is mainly made of basalt lavas. It forms the ocean floors.

Oceanic crust is much younger than continental crust. The oldest rocks in the continents are 3800 million years old, whereas no oceanic crust is older than 220 million years.

A

The inner core is solid because it is not quite as hot as the outer core.

B

The temperature in the Earth increases with depth.

Rocks in the mantle are brittle and break easily.

The density is highest in the mantle.

C

The Earth's core is big enough to form a planet on its own. It is about the same size as Mars.

D

E

The two types of crust are illustrated on the right.

5 Make a table to summarize the main differences between the two types of crust.

6 Where is the crust thickest?

7 How does the density of continental crust compare with that of the mantle below?

8 Here are some jumbled statements about oceanic and continental crust. Decide which statements refer to each type of crust.

  A It is 35 km thick on average.
  B It has a thickness of about 8 km.
  C It has the higher density of the two types of crust.
  D It usually forms land.
  E It is usually beneath the sea.
  F It contains the largest proportion of folded sediments.
  G It contains the largest proportion of metamorphic rocks.
  H It contains the largest proportion of igneous rocks.

9 Which type of crust do the rocks in the photograph on the right come from?

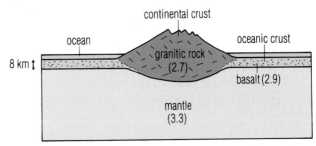

Continental and oceanic crust above the mantle. Figures in brackets are typical densities in g/cm³

The rock in this landscape is mainly gneiss

O 2.5 Drifting continents

Alfred Wegener was a scientist who suggested that the edges of some continents have shapes which can be fitted together like pieces of a jigsaw. He also found other features, such as rock structures and fossil deposits which he thought matched closely.

In 1915, Wegener put forward his theory of **continental drift**. He suggested that the continents are like huge rafts 'floating' on denser, more plastic material beneath them. Once, they had all been part of one huge supercontinent. This had split into pieces which had been slowly drifting apart ever since. Wegener believed that continental movements made rocks fold into mountain ranges: for example, the Himalayas had been formed because of the northward movement of India against the Asian continent.

At the top of the right-hand page, you can see two continents that Wegener believed were once joined.

1 Trace the shapes of the two continents onto thin card. Find out how well these continents might once have fitted together.
2 Did you find any evidence to support Wegener's theory? If so, what was it?
3 Can you think of any reasons why the coastlines might not be an exact fit?

The maps on the right show what Wegener thought the world looked like at four stages during the last 200 million years. The maps are not in the correct order.

4 Decide what order you think the maps should be in. Then decide which label belongs with each one.
5 According to Wegener's ideas, when did the Atlantic Ocean first start to form?
6 To which continent was Australia once joined?
7 When did India collide with Asia?
8 What do you think happened to the sediments which were once at the bottom of the ocean between India and Asia?
9 Coal is formed in tropical swamps. Yet coal seams have been found in Antarctica. Do you think that Wegener's theory can explain this? If so, how?

A

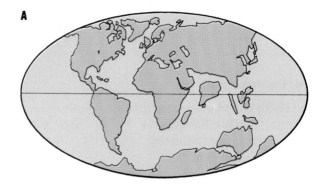

B

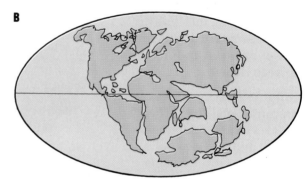

C

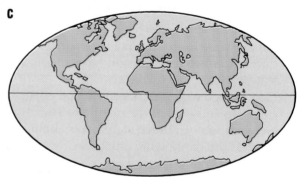

D

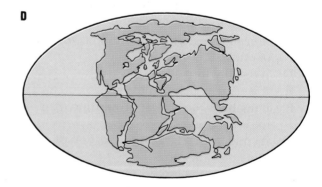

Which of these labels goes with each map?

200 million years ago	**55 million years ago**
120 million years ago	**Present**

40

For and against

When Wegener first put forward his theory, few scientists agreed with him. Most thought that the Earth was cooling and that its skin wrinkled into folds as it contracted.

10 Imagine that you are a journalist for a science magazine in 1915. Write an account describing the arguments and feelings of the scientists involved.

Signs of spreading

Ocean ridges form the longest and largest mountains on Earth, though they are mostly below sea level. In the 1950s, scientists started to study ocean ridges in more detail. They noticed that, at the crests of ridges, new rocks are being formed by volcanic activity. They have also found that, moving outwards either side of a ridge, the crust gets steadily older. The map on the right below shows the Mid–Atlantic ridge. The section shows the changes which scientists think are happening under the ridge and either side of it.

11 What is happening to the continental crust?

12 What is happening to the oceanic crust?

13 Where is the material for the new oceanic crust coming from?

14 In the oceanic crust, why are the rocks farther out from a ridge older than those closer in?

Scientists think that the ocean floor slowly moves outwards from a ridge as new oceanic crust is made by volcanoes and intrusions along the crest. They call this **sea-floor spreading**.

15 If scientists had known about sea-floor spreading in 1915, do you think they would have been more likely to support Wegener's ideas? Discuss this with your group.

Scientists have estimated that the Atlantic Ocean is widening at a rate of 3 cm per year. Use this estimate to help you answer the following.

16 How much wider will the Atlantic Ocean be in 1000 years time?

17 How much wider will it be in 1 million years time?

18 How much wider is the Atlantic now than when Christopher Columbus crossed it 500 years ago?

19 The North Atlantic is now 6000 km wide. Estimate when the ocean first started to form. How does this compare with the estimate you made using the maps on the opposite page?

20 Where do you think the oldest oceanic crust in the Atlantic is? How old is it?

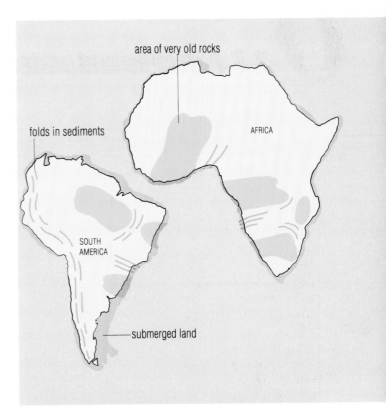

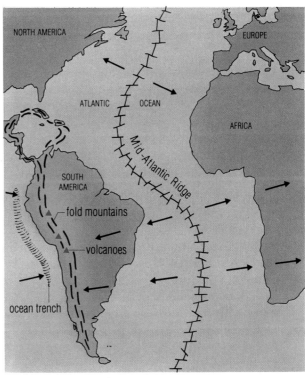

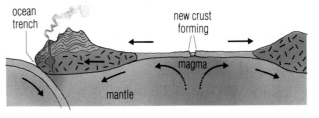

O 2.6 Patterns and plates

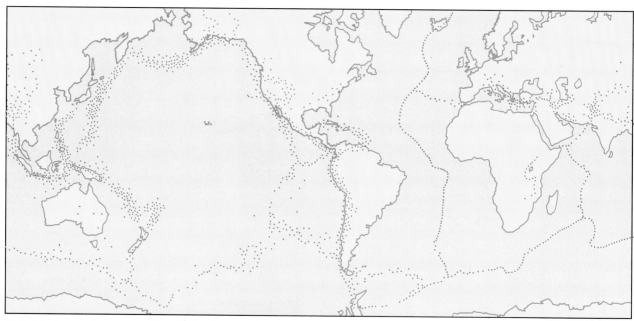

Each dot shows where an earthquake has happened in the last 20 years

In some parts of the world, earthquakes are rare events. In other places, they are very common. Look at the map above showing the distribution of earthquakes.

1 Were there more earthquakes on land or beneath the sea?
2 Can you see any pattern in the distribution of dots? If so, describe it.

Earth movements can make rocks fold to form mountain chains.

3 Find these fold mountain chains in an atlas: Rocky Mountains, Alps, Himalayas, Caucasus Mountains, Andes.
4 Does the distribution pattern of fold mountains match the earthquake pattern?
5 In an atlas, find a map showing volcanoes. Does their distribution follow a pattern?

Areas of the world where there are earthquakes, volcanoes, or chains of fold mountains being formed are called **active zones**.

6 Trace the coastal outline of the map above. On your tracing, shade in all the active zones you have found.
7 Why do you think some zones are active, while large areas of the world are inactive?

Plate tectonics

Scientists now think that the Earth's crust is divided into large sections which they call **plates**. These can slowly move over the denser, more plastic material beneath them. As one plate moves against others, earthquakes, volcanoes and folding may occur at the edges. The study of plate movements is called **plate tectonics**.

42

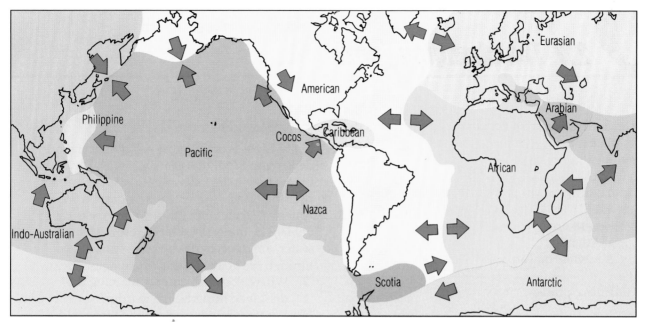

The world's plates and directions of movement

The map above shows the world's plates and directions of movement at their edges.

8 Which are the six largest plates? Which plate is the largest of all?

9 Place your tracing (the one showing active zones) over the plates map. How does it compare? Would you agree with the people on the opposite page?

10 Plates can be continental or oceanic crust, or both. Find an example of a plate whose surface is entirely oceanic crust.

Types of plate movement

The diagrams on the right show three types of plate movement.

11 Find an example of each type of movement in the map above.

12 Look again at the final diagram in spread O2.5. What is happening where the American and Nazca plates meet?

13 What are the diagrams below showing?

14 Draw your own version of the diagrams, adding the labels.

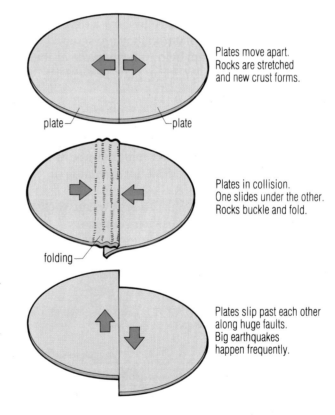

Plates move apart. Rocks are stretched and new crust forms.

Plates in collision. One slides under the other. Rocks buckle and fold.

Plates slip past each other along huge faults. Big earthquakes happen frequently.

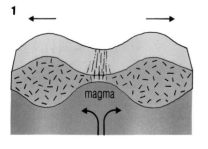

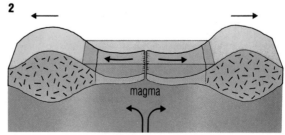

Labels:

South America
Africa
Atlantic Ocean
Mid–Atlantic Ridge
new ocean floor
volcanic activity
fissures

O 2.7 The changing Earth

The Earth's surface is constantly being changed by plate movements. New mountains form as sediments are folded. New oceans form, or old ones close, as plates move apart or together.

1 Look at the world map of plates in spread O2.6. Decide whether the following seas and oceans are opening or closing:
   a Atlantic   b Pacific
   c Mediterranean Sea d Red Sea

Colliding plates

When two plates meet, the weaker, thinner plate sinks under the stronger plate. There is considerable friction where the two plates rub together. The sediments have too low a density to sink with the weaker plate, so they are scraped off into folds. The diagram below shows parts of the Nazca plate and the American plate in western South America.

2 Draw a large version of the diagram.
3 Label the weaker sinking plate.
4 Why is there an ocean trench?
5 Where would you expect fold mountains to form? Use an atlas to find out the name of these fold mountains.
6 On your diagram, mark an area where rock movements might cause earthquakes.
7 Why do you think that one zone is very hot?
8 Mark in where these features might be:
   magma intrusions with volcanoes above
   metamorphic rocks
   fold mountains
   area of least disturbance.

Mineral deposits

Many of the world's most valuable metal ore deposits are found at plate margins. For example, there are rich deposits of gold, copper and tin near the Nazca-American boundary in South America. Many minerals form in cracks called **veins**. The minerals, which were dissolved in water, are deposited when the water flows through the veins. Look at the diagram below.

9 Where does the water containing the dissolved minerals come from?
10 What makes the water flow through the veins?
11 List some other regions of the world where you would expect valuable mineral deposits to be found.

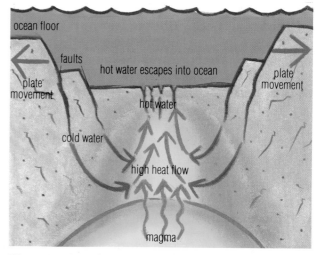

Water circulation at a plate boundary

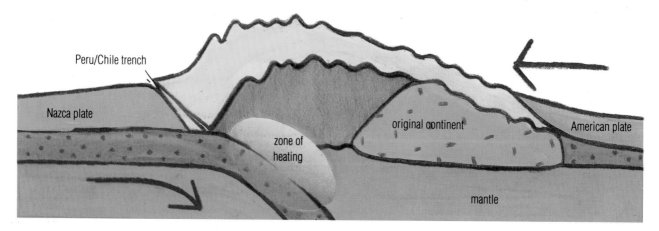

Then and now

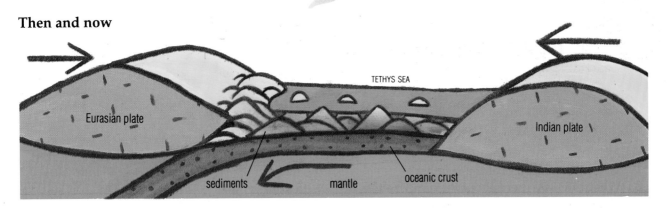

The section diagram above shows the ancient Tethys Ocean between the Indian plate and the Eurasian plate 50 million years ago.

12 What do you think will have happened to the plates since the time shown?

13 What do you think will have happened to the sea floor sediments?

14 Draw another diagram to show what you would expect the region to look like today.

15 The area you have drawn includes the Himalayan mountain range. Where do you think the Himalayas should be marked on your diagram?

Future Earth

See if you can predict how the surface of the Earth might look in 50 million years time!

You need
Thin card, scissors, tracing paper, outline map of the world's plates.

Things to think about
• Which plates will lose area and become smaller as they collide?
• Which plates will increase in surface area?
• How will these changes affect the positions of the continents?

What to do
■ Trace the plates onto thin card and cut them out.
■ Place your model plates in their correct positions on the plate map.
■ Decide how you think the plates will move. You will need to overlap your model plates where they collide.
■ Draw a sketch map to show what you think the Earth's surface might look like in 50 million years time.

Plate debate

Scientists think that the theory of plate tectonics is a better model for explaining the behaviour of the Earth's crust than Wegener's original theory of continental drift. But they expect that the plate theory will be developed further as more evidence is gathered.

16 Below are some students' comments about the theory of plate tectonics. Discuss these comments with your group, then write down your ideas about them. Compare your ideas with the rest of the class.

O *3.1 Wind and weather*

For some activities on this spread, you will need outline maps (or tracings) of Britain.

In each of the photographs below:
1 What are the effects of the weather?
2 What clues are there about the temperature, the wind, and the amount of water vapour carried by the air?

Where the wind blows

The weather we experience depends partly on the temperature of the air and its water content. This in turn, depends on where the air has come from. Air may have collected water vapour if it has recently passed over the sea. If air has a high water vapour content, scientists say that it has a high **humidity**.

3 On an outline map of Britain, show the directions in which you would expect each of the following to blow across Britain:

moist air   dry, warm air   cold air

4 Take it in turns to explain your choices to the rest of your group. Do you all agree?

Here is the forecast ...

Weather centres collect data from all over the country before preparing weather maps. Look at the map on the right and answer the following with your group:
5 What clue is there to the time of year?
6 What kinds of data must have been recorded before the map could be drawn?
7 What types of instruments would have been used?
8 Describe what the weather is like in the different regions of the country.
9 See if you can predict how the weather might change over the next three hours. Draw a map to show the new situation.

Three people ring up your weather centre. They want a forecast for the day and advice about their day's activities:

a A teacher from Bristol, planning a field trip to South Wales.
b A bricklayer in Glasgow who cannot work if it is frosty.
c A hang glider pilot in Birmingham.

10 In your group, work out a reply for each person.

46

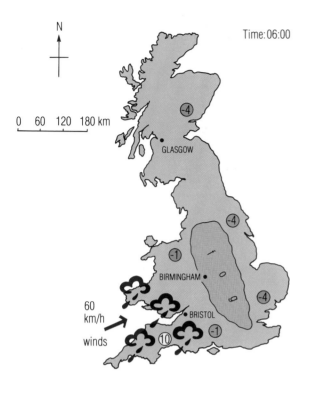

Time: 06:00

Changing wind

The **wind rose diagram** below gives hourly data about the wind over a 12 hour period.

11 What kinds of data about the wind are provided by this diagram?

12 In which hours were the highest wind speeds recorded?

13 What was the average wind speed over the 12 hour period?

14 What was the prevailing (most common) wind direction?

15 How did the wind direction change over the 12 hour period? You could answer this question by drawing sketches.

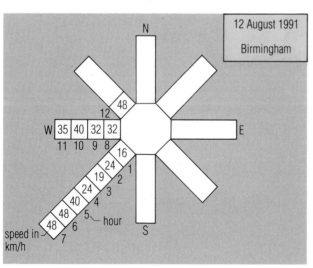

12 August 1991

Birmingham

Extremes of weather

Most of the time we do not think of the British weather as unusual, but sometimes there are exceptional conditions. Floods, high winds, tornadoes, blizzards, prolonged dry spells and drought are all extremes of weather which can be experienced in Britain.

The great storms of 1990

Late in January, Britain was hit by force 9 gales. Tiles were ripped off roofs and trees were blown down. Many buildings suffered structural damage. Forecasters were warning people of more to come and advising people to stay indoors. But this advice was of little use to some people in North Wales. At Towyn, waves driven by high tides and strong winds destroyed the sea wall, and thousands were forced to evacuate their homes. The severe flooding was made worse by heavy rain.

Look at the newspaper report above.

16 What examples of damage are mentioned?

17 What three aspects of the bad weather caused the damage?

18 What does the phrase 'force 9 gale' mean?

19 What direction do you think the storm might have come from? Why?

20 Prepare your own newspaper article describing another example of an unusual period of weather.

Forecast check

With your group:

■ Collect and cut out a sequence of newspaper weather forecast maps over a period of a few weeks.

■ Record what the weather was actually like in your region over this period.

■ Work out the accuracy of the forecasts over the period. You could express this as a percentage.

■ Find a way of presenting the maps and information you have collected and the conclusions you have reached.

O 3.2 Changing pressure

Weather forecasters often use the word 'pressure' when describing weather conditions. Discuss these with your group:

1 In what ways might the word 'pressure' feature in a weather report?
2 How do you think pressure affects the weather? Write down your ideas.

The instrument in the photograph on the right measures air pressure. It is called a **barometer**.

3 What kind of weather would you associate with a rise in air pressure?
4 What kind of weather would you associate with a fall in air pressure?

Heavy air?

The weight of air in the atmosphere causes the pressure in the air around us. The effects of this pressure can be seen if all the air is removed from an empty can with a vacuum pump.

5 If this is done, what happens to the can?
6 Which way does the pressure act? Is it downwards, or in other directions as well?

Now try this investigation:

■ Measure the mass of 500 cm³ (half a litre) of air. The diagram on the right shows you one way of doing this.
■ Estimate the total mass of air in the laboratory you are working in. See how this compares with your own mass and the mass of a medium-sized car (about 1000 kg).

Things to think about

• From the two measurements being made in the diagram, how could you work out the mass (in grams) of a litre of air?
• How could you measure the volume (in litres) of air in the laboratory? Hint: a one litre cube measures 10 cm x 10 cm x 10 cm.

The 'column' of atmosphere over the roof of your laboratory is more than 50 km deep. The air in it is about 2000 times heavier than the air inside the laboratory itself!

7 Estimate the total mass of air in the 'column' of atmosphere which lies above the roof of your laboratory.

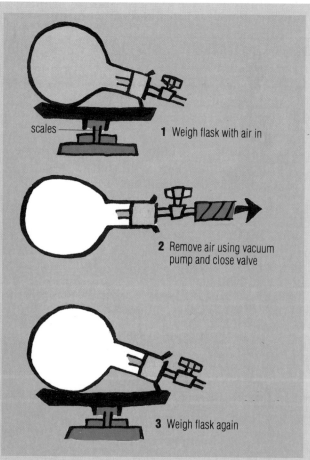

scales

1 Weigh flask with air in

2 Remove air using vacuum pump and close valve

3 Weigh flask again

Looking into barometers

The diagram on the right shows one simple type of barometer. It measures air pressure in **millibars (mb)**. In the barometer, there is a thin metal box with flexible sides. This is partly squashed by the pressure of the air outside.

8 Explain what happens in the instrument if there is a sudden rise in air pressure.

■ See if you can design and make your own barometer using everyday materials.

Things to think about
- Will your instrument have a pointer? If so, how will you make it move?
- How can you get your readings to match those from a manufactured instrument?

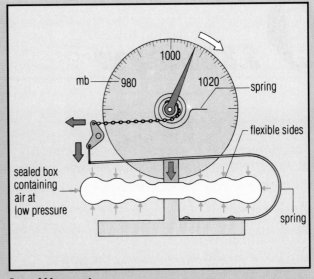

Aneroid barometer

Highs and lows

Air pressure is changing all the time as air moves from place to place. People talk about areas of 'high pressure' and 'low pressure' but the pressure difference between the two is not very great. Sinking air has a slightly higher pressure than average. Often, it is relatively dry and is associated with fine weather. Rising air has a slightly lower pressure than average. As it rises, it cools, and water vapour may condense to form clouds and rain. So areas of lower pressure often bring wet weather. Temperature changes can make air rise or sink. The diagram on the right shows another way in which air can be made to rise and sink.

9 Draw your own copy of the diagram. Use labels and symbols to show where you would expect the following to be:
rising air   sinking air
rain   dry weather
clouds

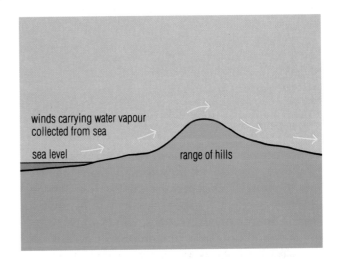

Look at the Atlantic weather map on the right. The lines on the map are called **isobars**. They join points of equal pressure. The numbers are pressures in millibars.

10 Decide whether each of the areas A, B and C is of low pressure or high pressure.

11 Say whether you think the air is rising or sinking in each of these.

12 Describe what you think the weather might be like over Britain and over Iceland.

13 Describe how you think the weather over Britain and Iceland might change during the following few days.

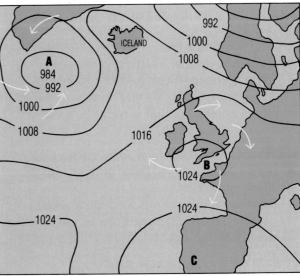

Noon: February 2. **A** will move north-east and deepen. **B** will move east. **C** will remain almost stationary.

O 3.3 Moving air

Investigating convection

Temperature differences can make air move. Air movements caused by heat are called **convection currents**.

- Use a lighted candle to set up a convection current. The diagram on the right shows you how to do this.
- Use smoke to see which way the air is moving. Record what you see.

Look at the air labelled A and the air labelled B in the diagram.
1 Which is hotter and which is cooler?
2 Which is rising and which is sinking?
3 Which is higher pressure and which is lower pressure?
4 Which direction does the air flow: from high pressure to low, or the other way?

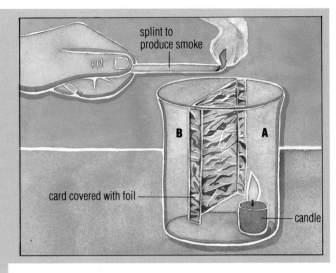

Winds are air movements in the atmosphere. However, they do not flow straight from high to low pressure. This is because the Earth's rotation also has an effect. It tends to make winds move in spirals. In low pressure zones, winds spiral inwards and upwards. In high pressure areas, they spiral outwards and downwards.

Look at the wind diagram on the right.
5 Which do you think is the high pressure area and which the low?
6 Which is warmer, the land or the sea?
7 During the day, land heats up more quickly than the sea. Why do you think you can often feel a breeze blowing in from the sea when you are on a beach?

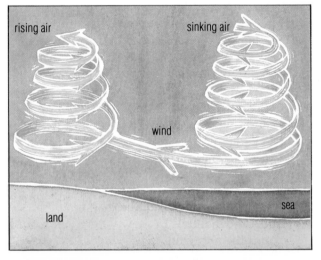

Look back at the Atlantic map in spread O3.2.
8 Can you see any evidence of wind spiralling? If so, where?
9 Do the spirals support your ideas about which were high pressure areas and which were low?

Look at the diagram on the right.
10 Why is it hotter at the equator than at the poles?
11 Where do you think air might be sinking and air rising?

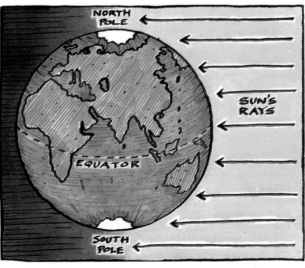

Cells and climates

In the 18th century, George Hadley suggested that the Earth might have huge air circulation systems called **convection cells**. He thought that air would rise above the Equator, flow north and south, cool, and sink at the poles. Scientists now know that air cools and sinks long before it reaches the poles. What actually happens is shown on the right.

12 How many convection cells are there?

13 How do you think that present-day scientists have been able to find out more about the atmosphere than George Hadley.

14 Draw your own version of the diagram. Mark in the zones of high and low pressure.

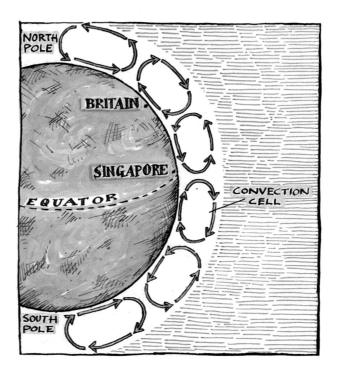

The world's climates can be classified into four main types:

A Hot and dry (for example, deserts)
B Hot and wet (for example, rain forests)
C Cool and wet (for example, Northern Europe)
D Cold and dry (for example, polar regions)

15 Why do you think the Earth has four main types of climate? Can you decide which type of climate each pressure zone has?

The tables show climate data for Singapore and for Birmingham, Britain.

16 Present the two groups of data in the form of graphs or charts.

17 See if you can decide which table is for which place.

18 See if you can decide which of the four types of climate each represents.

Climate data A

°C	27	28	29	28	27	27	27	28	29	29	28	26
Rainfall in mm	230	170	180	195	170	160	170	200	170	200	230	270
Month	J	F	M	A	M	J	J	A	S	O	N	D

Climate data B

°C	4	4	6	8	11	14	17	16	13	9	6	4
Rainfall in mm	51	43	48	43	56	58	58	68	46	71	61	68
Month	J	F	M	A	M	J	J	A	S	O	N	D

Local conditions

Within a climate zone, local conditions can vary from day to day. The map on the right shows five types of air flow which Britain can experience.

19 Which type do you think is most common?

20 For each type of air flow in summer, choose two of the following words to describe it (for example: *warm* and *wet*).

wet cool dry warm hot

Sometimes, an area of slowly sinking air can remain stationary over Britain for weeks.

21 Would you expect much cloud to form if air is sinking?

22 Will the pressure be high or low?

23 What kind of weather would this bring:
a in summer?
b in winter?

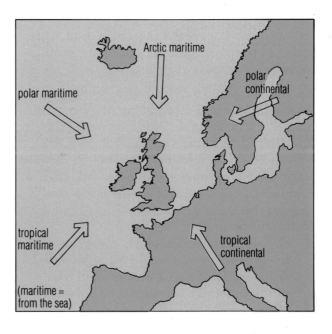

3.4 Fronts and the weather

In an area of low pressure, warm air spirals upwards as it rises over cooler, denser air. The two air masses do not mix easily. The boundaries between them are called **fronts**.

Modelling a front

Use warm water and cold water to model a front. Investigate what happens when the two water masses meet.

You need
Water tank with a removable partition, warm tap water, cold salty water (the salt makes it more dense), red and blue dyes.

What to do
- Fill one side of the tank with warm water and the other with cold.
- Use the dyes to colour the two types of water. Which colour will you use for which?
- Carefully remove the partition.
  What happens? Is there any evidence of a front? If so, how does it change?

1 What will happen when a mass of warm air meets a mass of cooler, denser air?

Atlantic fronts

As warm, moist air rises at a front, it cools. This makes some of the water vapour condense to form cloud and rain.

The diagrams on the right show what happens when a mass of cold air from the Arctic meets a mass of warm, moist air from the tropics. The warm, moist air forms a wedge with cold air on either side. As the wedge drifts along, its forward 'edge' is a **warm front**, and its rearward 'edge' is a **cold front**. On a weather map, the fronts are shown as lines though, really, they are boundaries which stretch up from sea level.

2 On your own version of the lower diagram, shade in where you would expect there to be most cloud and rain. Draw in where you would expect the pressure to be lowest.

3 Why are the fronts called *warm* and *cold*?

Europe, with a depression over the British Isles

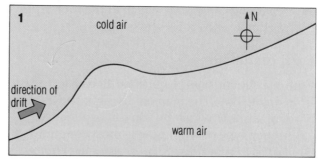

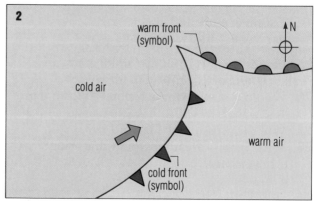

52

Depressions

Low pressure systems are called **depressions** or 'lows'. You can see a depression, with its fronts, in the weather map on the right.

4 In some places, the isobars are very close together. What does this tell you about the way the pressure changes? What type of wind conditions would you expect in these places?

5 What type of weather do you think Britain is experiencing?

Depression problems

Some friends arrived to take part in a sports event in Birmingham at midday. But they had problems during the afternoon because of the weather. The diagram below shows a section through the depression that was affecting them. It was moving from west to east at 10 kilometres per hour.

6 Describe the weather which they experienced during the next four hours. Remember to describe what the sky looked like and how the weather changed during the afternoon.

7 At about what times during the afternoon was it raining?

8 Which of the two fronts gave the longer period of heavy rain?

The table on the right shows the rainfall from another depression which passed over Birmingham a few days later. This depression was also moving at 10 kilometres per hour.

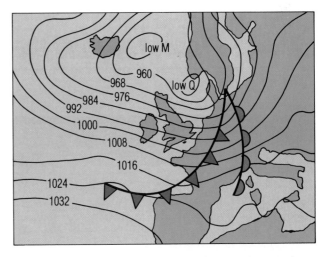

Time	Rainfall in mm	Time	Rainfall in mm
9:00	0	13:30	1
9:30	1	14:00	1
10:00	3	14:30	2
10:30	9	15:00	5
11:00	13	15:30	8
11:30	8	16:00	14
12:00	5	16:30	6
12:30	2	17:00	3
13:00	0	17:30	1

9 Use the data to draw a bar graph.

10 At about what times did the warm and cold fronts pass over the city?

11 How did this depression compare in size with the earlier one?

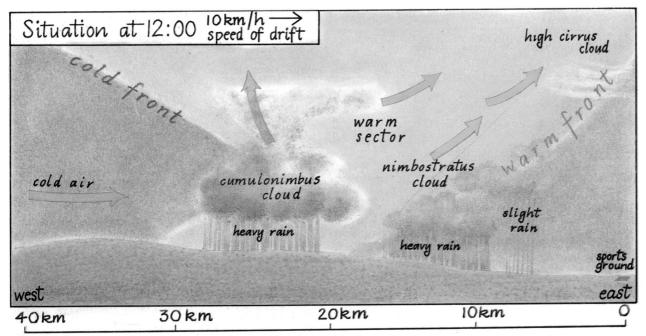

Situation at 12:00   10km/h → speed of drift

high cirrus cloud

cold front

warm sector

cold air

cumulonimbus cloud

nimbostratus cloud

warm front

heavy rain

heavy rain

slight rain

sports ground

west   east

40km   30km   20km   10km   0

4.1 Planets around the Sun

100 000 km

Pluto Neptune Uranus Saturn Sun Jupiter Mars Earth Venus Mercury

Look at the diagram above with your group. The Sun and the planets have been drawn to scale. But the planets are not at their correct distances from the Sun.

1 Which of the objects in the diagram is a star?
2 Why do most stars look much smaller than this one?
3 Draw your own version of the diagram to show the positions of the planets and how they move through space. To simplify the diagram, you could draw the Sun at a reduced size.
4 Make a chart to show what you think the following mean:

   planet   moon
   Solar System   star
   galaxy   Universe

The inner planets

Mercury, Venus, Earth and Mars are sometimes called the **inner planets.** Three of them are shown in the photographs on this spread.

5 Why do you think Mercury, Venus, Earth and Mars are all called the inner planets?
6 Why in the photograph on the right, is part of the planet in shadow?
7 One of the four inner planets does not have an atmosphere. Which one? What clues did you use to decide that it has no atmosphere?

8 Can you suggest reasons why the planet in question 7 does not have an atmosphere?
9 Earth and Mars both have polar caps. Can you suggest reasons why the two other planets do *not* have polar caps?
10 What other similarities and differences do you think there are between the four inner planets? Discuss this with your group and list your ideas.

Mercury
(composite photograph)

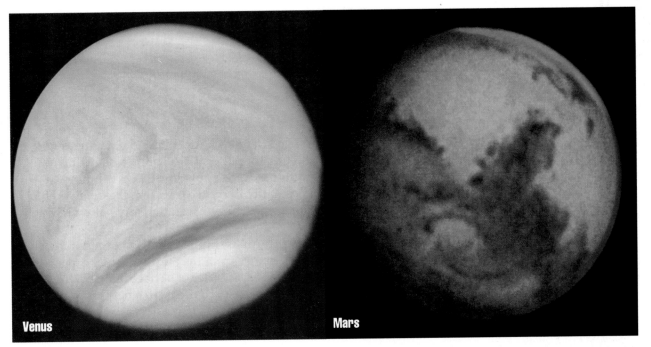

Venus

Mars

Orbits

The path a planet follows as it moves round the Sun is called its **orbit**. Most planets have orbits which are approximately circular.

11 What force keeps the planets in orbit round the Sun?

12 How does this force change as distances from the Sun increase?

The average distance from the Earth to the Sun is 150 million kilometres. Astronomers call this distance one **astronomical unit (AU)**. Look at the table on the right.

13 As distances from the Sun increase, what happens to the time it takes a planet to complete one orbit?

14 One piece of information is missing from the table. With your group, estimate the time it takes Uranus to travel once round the Sun. You will first need to decide on the best way of doing this.

15 Use the information in the table to make a chart or model showing the distances between the Sun and the planets to scale.

Look at the bottom table on the right.

16 Use the information in the table to make a drawing or a model showing the Sun, the Earth, the Moon and the distances between them to scale.

17 Why do you think sending manned missions to other planets is so much more difficult than sending them to the Moon?

Planet	Average distance from the Sun in AU	Time for one orbit in years
Mercury	0.4	0:2
Venus	0.7	0.6
Earth	1.0	1.0
Mars	1.5	1.9
Jupiter	5.2	11.9
Saturn	9.5	29.5
Uranus	19.2	
Neptune	30.1	164.8
Pluto	39.4	247.7

Diameter of Sun	1 390 000 km
Diameter of Moon	3480 km
Diameter of Earth	12 800 km
Average distance from Earth to Sun	150 000 000 km
Average distance from Earth to Moon	384 000 km

4.2 Exploring the planets

Data search

Imagine that a spacecraft is being launched on a mission which will take astronauts to all the planets in the Solar System. The mission will take many years.

■ Your group's task is to gather data on the planets for the ship's computer. Some data is given below. You should be able to collect more from other sources (including spreads O4.1 and O4.3). When you have all your data, prepare and present a file giving information on each of the planets.

Things to think about
- How will you present the information on each planet?
- Could you use a computer database to store the information?
- As a group, will you organize things so that different people take on different tasks?

Looking for patterns

When scientists have collected data, they start looking for patterns. Sometimes, they find patterns which apply in *most* cases but not necessarily in *every* case. From the data you have collected, see if you can find any patterns which apply in most cases:

1 Make a list of the planets in order of their distance from the Sun. Then make a list of the planets in order of surface temperature. Can you see a pattern? If so, what is it? And how would you explain it?
2 Now see if you can see patterns linking any of the following:
   - density
   - distance from the Sun
   - diameter
   - surface gravity.
3 Make a poster to present your results. Then compare your results with other groups.

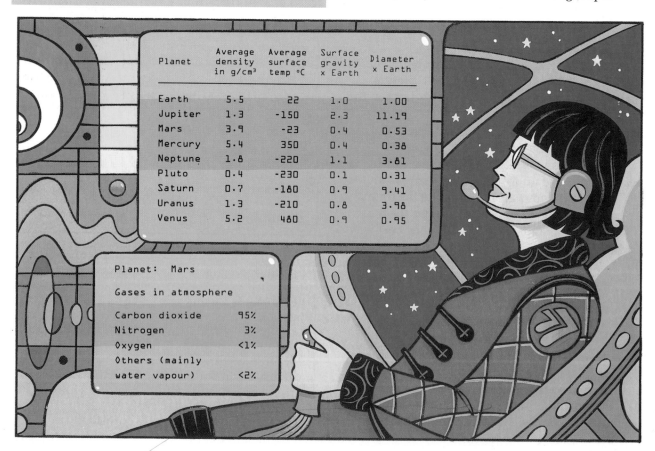

Planet	Average density in g/cm³	Average surface temp °C	Surface gravity x Earth	Diameter x Earth
Earth	5.5	22	1.0	1.00
Jupiter	1.3	-150	2.3	11.19
Mars	3.9	-23	0.4	0.53
Mercury	5.4	350	0.4	0.38
Neptune	1.8	-220	1.1	3.81
Pluto	0.4	-230	0.1	0.31
Saturn	0.7	-180	0.9	9.41
Uranus	1.3	-210	0.8	3.98
Venus	5.2	480	0.9	0.95

Planet: Mars

Gases in atmosphere

Carbon dioxide	95%
Nitrogen	3%
Oxygen	<1%
Others (mainly water vapour)	<2%

Mercury

Mercury is too small to have an atmosphere. Its surface is covered with craters. Being so close to the Sun, the planet is very difficult to observe from Earth.

Mercury takes 88 days to orbit the Sun. Until about 30 years ago, scientists thought that it also took 88 days to turn once on its axis and always kept the same face to the Sun. If the scientists of 30 years ago had been right:

4 What do you think day and night would have been like at different places on Mercury?
5 How would you expect the temperature on Mercury's surface to have varied?

From radar measurements, scientists now know that Mercury turns once in 59 days.

6 Describe what you think day and night is really like on Mercury and how the temperature on the surface might vary.

Venus

Venus has a very dense atmosphere of mainly carbon dioxide gas. It acts as an insulating blanket and traps the Sun's radiant heat. This is an example of the greenhouse effect.

In 1982, the unmanned Soviet spacecraft *Venera 14* passed through clouds of sulphuric acid droplets in the Venusian atmosphere to land and take pictures of a dry, rocky surface. It recorded an atmospheric pressure 90 times greater than at the Earth's surface.

7 What do you think would be the problems of landing astronauts on Venus?

View from a spacecraft on the surface of Mars

Mars

Mars has polar caps which are a mixture of frozen carbon dioxide and ice. The planet has a very thin atmosphere. It is very dry with violent duststorms.

9 Why might scientists think that there are winds on Mars?
10 From the data on the opposite page, would you expect there to be a greenhouse effect on Mars? Explain your answer.
11 Now compare the surface temperatures of Mars and Venus. How do you think the difference might be explained?
12 Olympus Mons is a volcano on Mars. It is 500 km wide and 25 km high. The Earth's largest volcano, Mauna Kea in Hawaii, is 310 km wide and 9 km high. Draw a diagram to show how the two volcanoes compare in size.

Venusian gas

Find out more about one of Venus's gases: carbon dioxide.

■ Place a candle in a beaker and light it.
■ Remove the top from a gas jar full of carbon dioxide. *Very* slowly tip the gas into the beaker. What happens when you do this?
■ What does your experiment tell you about carbon dioxide?
■ Could you improve your experiment to test any of your findings more thoroughly?

8 Where in the Venusian atmosphere would you expect the carbon dioxide to be most concentrated, high up or low down?

O 4.3 Exploring further

To answer the questions on this spread, you may need information from spreads O4.1 and O4.2.

Many of the planets in the Solar System have moons in orbit around them. Some of the planets also have rings. The table beneath the photograph on the right tells you which planets have moons and rings. The rings are only a few kilometres thick, and they are not one solid mass. They consist of billions of fragments of ice ranging from a few millimetres in size up to several metres. Each of these fragments is a tiny 'moonlet' in its own orbit.

1 Which planet has the most moons?
2 Which planet has the brightest rings?
3 Can you see any patterns linking the number of moons with other data about the planets? Write down your ideas and compare them with other groups.

Planet watch

Most of the 'dots' which you can see in the night sky are stars. But a few are planets. If you see an especially bright dot in the sky it is likely to be either Jupiter or Venus. Using binoculars, it is usually possible to tell which is which. When Venus is nearest Earth, it may just be possible to see a crescent shape. Jupiter can be seen as a very small disc, with four tiny dots near it. These are Jupiter's four largest moons: Ganymede, Callisto, Io and Europa. Three of them (Ganymede, Callisto and Io) are larger than our own Moon.

■ Look at Jupiter through binoculars. Can you see its four largest moons?
■ Look at Venus through binoculars. Is it possible to see a crescent shape?

4 Why do you think that Jupiter and Venus are the brightest planets seen in the sky?
5 Why do the distances of the planets from Earth change?
6 Why do you think that Venus sometimes appears to have a crescent shape?
7 If people study the sky night after night for several months, how can they tell (even without binoculars) which are stars and which are planets?

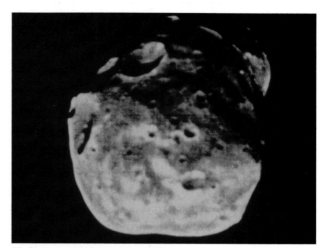

Phobos, one of the moons of Mars

Planet	Moons and rings
Mercury	0
Venus	0
Earth	1
Mars	2
Jupiter	16 + faint rings
Saturn	23 + clear rings
Uranus	15 + faint rings
Neptune	8 + faint rings
Pluto	1

Minor planets

Between the orbits of Mars and Jupiter are thousands of minor planets called **asteroids**. The five largest are listed in the table below.

8 Which is the largest of the minor planets? Draw a diagram to show how it compares in size with the Earth.
9 Like most moons, none of the minor planets has an atmosphere. Why do you think this is?

Asteroid	Diameter in km
Vesta	549
Pallas	538
Ceres	1020
Davida	341
Interamnia	339

The five largest asteroids (minor planets)

Jupiter

Jupiter has more matter in it than the rest of the planets put together. Scientists think that Jupiter is largely made up of hydrogen gas. It has a rocky core, but no solid surface. One prominent feature is the Great Red Spot (bottom left in the photo).

10 From the information you have seen, what clues are there to suggest that Jupiter might not have a solid surface?

11 What kind of feature would you expect the Great Red Spot to be?

12 Jupiter's day is only 10 hours long. What clues are there to suggest that Jupiter is turning quickly on its axis?

Saturn

Like Jupiter, Saturn is mainly made up of hydrogen gas surrounding a rocky core. It is colder than Jupiter and has less turbulent weather systems. Even so, it has winds which blow at 14 000 km per hour.

13 Why do you think that Saturn is colder than Jupiter?

14 What are Saturn's rings made of?

Uranus

Uranus was discovered by William Herschel in 1781. He made the discovery using a telescope which he had built himself. It was the first new planet to be identified since ancient times and Herschel's discovery caused great excitement when it was announced. Uranus is largely made of methane gas. The planet is unusual in that its axis is tilted at more than 90°.

15 Why do you think that no-one knew of the existence of Uranus in ancient times?

Neptune

Like Uranus, Neptune has a rocky core, surrounded by water, liquid methane and ammonia, and an atmosphere mainly of methane gas. Scientists predicted the existence of Neptune before it was discovered. Observing Uranus, they found that its orbit varied from the course expected. They thought that this might be due to the gravitational pull of another unknown planet, and calculated where this planet should be. In 1846, the astronomer Johann Galle located the planet close to the position which had been calculated.

16 Why was Neptune not discovered until after Uranus?

Jupiter

Saturn

Pluto

This tiny planet is probably a ball of frozen methane. It has a moon called **Charon** which is about half its size: the two are really a double planet. Pluto follows an elliptical orbit, so its distance from the Sun varies. Part of its orbit passes inside Neptune's. Pluto is on this part at present and will continue to be so until 1999.

17 Which planet is now furthest from the Sun?

18 When will that situation change?

O 4.4 Orbits and gravity

Thought experiment

Here is a 'thought experiment' for you to try with your group. Before you carry it out, you will first need to draw a larger version of the lower part of the diagram on the right. This shows the Earth, with a tower so tall that its top is just above the atmosphere.

What to do

- Imagine that you have just dropped a heavy metal ball from the top of the tower. Where will it fall? Draw its path in pencil on your diagram.
- Now imagine that you have thrown the ball gently sideways from the top of the tower. How will it move this time? Draw it in.
- Now imagine that you have thrown the ball sideways a little faster than before. How will the ball move this time?
- Keep drawing what you think would happen as you throw the ball sideways faster and faster each time. Remember: there is no air to slow the ball, and you have superhuman muscles, so the ball's speed can be as fast as you like!

When one group carried out this thought experiment, someone claimed that, at one particular speed, the ball 'behaved like a satellite'.

1 What do you think they meant by 'behaved like a satellite'?
2 Would you agree with them?
3 If you were holding the ball at the top of the tower, you would feel the force of gravity pulling on it. Would the pull be any different if the tower were much taller? If so, how?

Look at the article on the right about the launch of *Sputnik 1*.

4 What do you think would have happened to the satellite if it had been launched at too high a speed?
5 What do you think would have happened if the speed had been too low?
6 In your thought experiment with the tower and the ball, at what speed would you have had to throw the ball to put it in orbit?

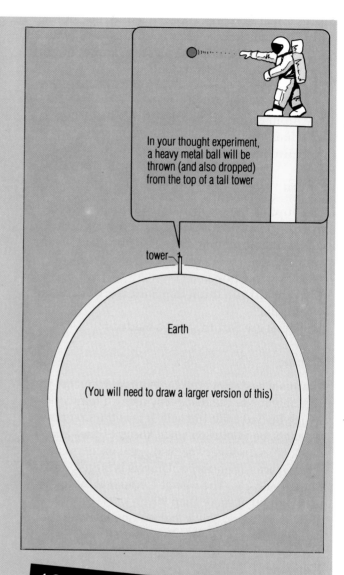

In your thought experiment, a heavy metal ball will be thrown (and also dropped) from the top of a tall tower

tower—

Earth

(You will need to draw a larger version of this)

4 October 1957

Sputnik launched

Today, the Russians successfully put the world's first artificial satellite into a low orbit around the Earth. The satellite was carried by a powerful launch rocket, which accelerated upwards, then gently tipped over until it was travelling horizontally just above the Earth's atmosphere at a speed of 8 km per second. This is the speed needed by all satellites to maintain a low orbit, no matter how heavy they are. Precision was essential. Any faster, and the satellite would

Pulled by gravity

The gravitational pull of the Earth holds satellites in orbit around it. Similarly, the gravitational pull of the Sun holds the Earth and the other planets in their orbits around it.

7 The Moon is sometimes described as a natural satellite of the Earth. What do you think this means?

Isaac Newton (1642-1727) was the first to realise that gravity is a force between *all* things. There is even a tiny gravitational attraction between you and the person next to you! But it is far too small to measure with normal instruments. Something has to be as massive as a planet or a moon before the gravitational pull is strong enough to have any effect. According to Newton:

- All masses attract each other. The more mass each has, the stronger the attraction.
- The further apart the masses are, the weaker the attraction between them.

8 Was your answer to question **3** in agreement with Newton's ideas?

9 Which do you think is more strongly attracted to the Sun: *Venus* or *Earth*? How did you decide on your answer?

Comets are collections of ice and gas which orbit the Sun. Their orbits are elliptical. Look at the diagram on the right.

10 Where do you think the Sun's gravitational pull on Halley's comet is strongest?

11 Where do you think the pull is weakest?

12 Where is Halley's comet travelling at its
   a highest speed   **b** lowest speed

Halley's comet

Testing an idea

Sandra is an amateur astronomer. She has a theory that the further a planet is from the Sun, the lower its speed of orbit will be.

- Is Sandra right? See if you can find out for yourself. You will need to check on the tables of data on the planets in earlier spreads. You will also need a calculator, because the calculations are difficult!

Things to think about

- Could you start by checking data about two planets at different distances from the Sun?
- How could you calculate how far each planet travels in one complete orbit?
- What else will you need to know to calculate the speed of the planet?

13 Which planet in the Solar System has the highest orbital speed around the Sun?

14 Which planet has the lowest orbital speed?

15 Which do you think has the highest orbital speed around the Earth, an artificial satellite a few hundred kilometres from the surface, or the Moon? Why?

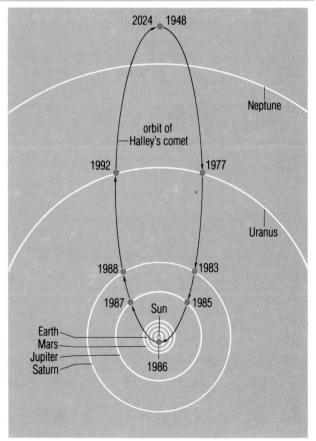

Orbit of Halley's comet (1948-2024)

O 4.5 Looking into tides

Tides are changes in the level of the oceans. Sue and Tim are especially interested in tides because they are sand yachters and they need wide stretches of flat, dry beach to race on. The trouble with many flat beaches is that the tide comes in a long way. Tim's tide timetable on the right is torn. So he is having trouble working out the best times for racing. Can you help ...?

Date	Time of high tide	Time of low tide
6 May	6:34	10:24
	18:59	12:46
7 May	7:24	1:11
	19:49	13:36
8 May	8:14	
	20:39	

1 When would be the best times for racing on 6 May and 7 May? Give your reasons.
2 Can you see any pattern in the tide times?
3 What would you predict to be the best time for racing on 8 May?
4 How many high tides are there in a 24 hour period?
5 How much later is each high tide time than the one before?
6 What would you estimate the missing low tide times for 8 May to be?

Scientists think that tides are mainly caused by the gravitational pull of the Moon. The diagram on the right shows what they think happens. The pull is strongest on the side of the Earth nearest to the Moon, so the water on that side (A) bulges outwards slightly. On the opposite side (B), the Moon's gravitational pull is weaker than on most of the Earth, so the water is 'left behind' to produce a second bulge. As the Earth rotates on its axis, each place passes in and out of the bulges, so the sea level rises and falls.

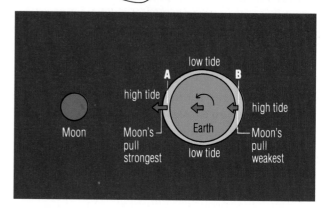

Discuss the following with your group, then compare answers with other groups:

7 Why might you expect there to be two high tides and two low tides every day?
8 If the Earth rotates once every 24 hours, why do you think it is *more* than 12 hours from one high tide to the next?

March

Date	1	2	3	4	5	6	7	8	9	10	11	12	13	14	15	16	17	18	19	20	21	22	23	24	25	26	27
Tidal range in metres	12.7	12.8	12.1	11.7	11.3	10.9	10.5	10.1	9.5	8.7	8.6	9.0	9.5	10.3	11.1	12.1	12.4	12.6	12.5	12.0	11.5	10.4	9.5	9.4	9.5	9.9	10.5
Phase of the Moon	○								◑							●						◐					

April

28	29	30	31	1	2	3	4	5	6	7	8	9	10	11	12	13	14	15	16	17	18	19	20	21	22	23	24	25	26	27	28	29	30
11.3	12.1	12.7	12.8	12.1	11.5	11.0	10.5	10.0	9.5	8.7	8.6	9.0	9.5	9.9	10.4	11.1	12.1	12.4	12.6	12.5	12.0	11.5	10.5	9.6	9.5	9.6	9.9	10.5	11.3	12.1	12.7	12.8	12.1
○					◑						●						◐										○						

Key: ● New Moon ◑ First quarter ● Full Moon ◐ Last quarter

Tidal range at Cardiff, March and April 1991

Comparing tides

Some high tides are higher than others. The table on the opposite page shows the **tidal range** at Cardiff for two months. The tidal range is the difference in level between low and high tide. The table also shows the **phases** of the Moon. These are our different views of the Moon as it orbits the Earth.

9   Why does the portion of the Moon which we see in shadow keep changing?

10 On what dates do the *highest* high tides occur?

11 Draw a graph to show how the tidal range at Cardiff varied over the two months.

12 Can you see any pattern linking the tidal range and the phases of the Moon?

The *highest* high tides are called **spring tides**. The *lowest* high tides are called **neap tides**. Scientists have a theory about why spring and neap tides occur. They think that the Sun's gravitational pull also affects the tides, though not so much as the Moon's. You can see their idea in diagrams below. Sometimes, the Earth, Moon and Sun are lined up so that the Sun's gravitational pull makes the bulges even bigger. At other times, the Sun's pull is at right angles to the pull of the Moon. This reduces the size of the bulges.

13 Mark the spring tides and neap tides on the graph you drew for question **11**.

14 Does the tidal range data for Cardiff support the scientists' ideas shown in the diagrams? Discuss this with your group and write down your ideas.

15 In diagram **B**, why do you think the Sun's pull reduces the size of the bulges?

The Severn Bore

The Severn Bore is a 'tidal wave' of water which regularly travels up the River Severn. It can be as much as 3 metres high. The bore occurs when a rising tide is funnelled into the narrowing Severn Estuary. This sets off a wave which travels up the river at about 5 m/s (10 mph). The size of the bore depends on the size of the tide. Strong winds can help produce a higher tide and a higher bore.

Cardiff is near the Severn Estuary. Use its tidal range data to help you answer the following:

16 On what dates in the table would you expect the highest bores?

17 Strong south-westerly gales were forecast for 15 March and 1 April. On which of these dates would there have been the biggest threat to local people living on low ground near the river? Why?

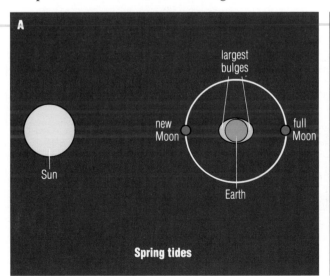

Spring tides

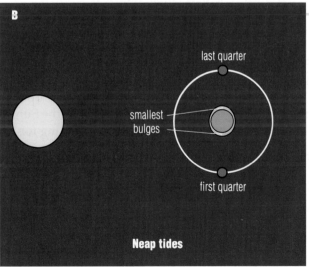

Neap tides

Depending on the position of the Moon, the Sun's gravitational pull may add to the bulging effect on the oceans or reduce it.

O *4.6 The Sun*

The Sun is our nearest star. It is 150 million km from Earth. The next nearest star, Proxima Centauri, is 300 000 times further away! The Sun is small compared with some stars. Yet its diameter (1 400 000 km) is about 100 times that of the Earth. The Sun is a ball of hot, glowing gas. 70% is hydrogen. The rest is mainly helium, but about 1% is made up of over 70 other elements.

1 Why is the Sun so much closer than other stars?
2 Make a drawing to show how the sizes of the Sun and the Earth compare.
3 Draw a pie chart to show the main gases in the Sun.
4 With your group, list all the ways the Sun affects the Earth and the planets. Make a poster to show your ideas. Here are some words to start you thinking:
   winds   life   orbit   seasons

   Compare your ideas with other groups. Which ones do you agree on?

The Sun's energy

The Sun radiates huge amounts of energy which give us light and heat on Earth. The energy comes from nuclear reactions in the core of the Sun, where the temperature reaches more than 15 million °C. At the surface, the temperature is around 6000 °C. The Sun's 'fuel' is hydrogen gas, but its energy is not released by burning. Instead, the extreme pressure and temperature in the core force hydrogen atoms together so that their nuclei (centres) combine and atoms of helium gas are created. This process is called **fusion**. It releases huge amounts of energy which were locked up in the hydrogen nuclei. Scientists think that the Sun has enough nuclear energy to keep it shining for another 5000 million years.

5 What is the source of the Sun's energy?
6 Why do you think that the pressure in the centre of the Sun is so high?
7 Why do you think the Sun is much hotter in its core than at its surface?
8 Use the information on this page to make a large diagram or chart about the Sun and its energy.

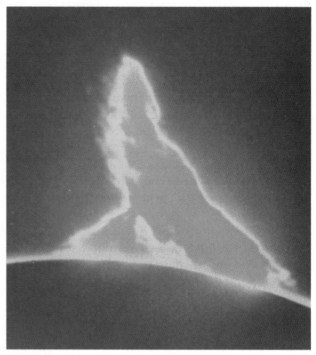

Solar flare

Solar flares

The photograph above shows a huge cloud of gas erupting from the Sun's surface. This is called a **solar flare**. It shoots out streams of charged atomic particles that can reach Earth. When the particles pass through the Earth's magnetic field, they cause a flickering glow in the upper atmosphere called an **aurora**.

9 See if you can use the photograph above to estimate the size of the solar flare.
10 What force pulls the gases in a solar flare back to the Sun?

Aurora borealis (the Northern Lights)

Looking for sunspots

Sunspots are areas on the Sun's surface which are not quite so hot as the rest. In pictures, they look like tiny dark patches on the surface of the Sun. But they are not really dark. They are just less bright than the areas around them. And they are not tiny! Most could swallow up the Earth many times over!

Safety warning!
It is extremely dangerous to look directly at the Sun. It can permanently damage your eyes. The only safe way to study the Sun is to project its image onto paper or card.

- Use a pair of binoculars (or a telescope) to project an image of the Sun onto a piece of white card. The diagram shows you how.
- Look for sunspots in the image. Draw on the card to record the position of the sunspots.
- If possible, study sunspots at regular times over a period of weeks. From your observations, you may be able to work out how long it takes the Sun to turn on its axis!

Useful information
To project the best image:
- Use only one side of the binoculars.
- Hold the card about 20-30 cm from the binocular eyepiece.
- Start with the eyepiece screwed out as far as it will go. Gradually screw it inwards until you have a clearly-focused image of the Sun.
- The black card around the eyepiece is not essential, but it shades the card so that the image is easier to see.

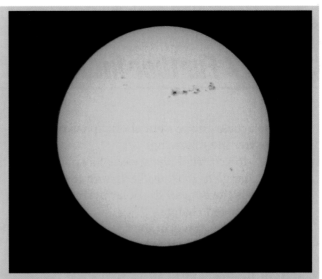

Sunspots

Camera obscura

Over a thousand years ago, the Arabs and the Chinese discovered how to project the image of the Sun into a darkened room. 500 years later, the idea was used in Europe in a device called a **camera obscura**. You can see the principle below. A small hole is used to project the image of the Sun onto a screen.

- Try making your own camera obscura. Find out how suitable it is for studying sunspots.

Things to think about
- Could you use a box or tube to shade the card screen?
- How will you cut the box or tube so that you can see the screen inside?
- Will you change the length of the box or tube to see which gives the biggest image?
- Will the size of the pin-hole affect the image?

O 4.7 Further into space

Read the article on the right about space travel. Then answer the following:

1 How do you think the speed of a spacecraft will change as it leaves Earth and travels towards the edge of the Solar System? Why will its speed change?

2 Radio waves travel at the speed of light. What problems would there be in holding a radio conversation with astronauts in a spacecraft near Jupiter?

3 How long does it take light from the star Proxima Centauri to reach Earth?

4 What is the shortest possible time for a round trip to Proxima Centauri and back? Why would a real trip take many thousands of times longer than this?

Star ideas

Below are three of the scientists who helped develop our understanding of the stars. But they are not in the correct sequence.

5 In which of these years do you think each statement might have been made?
   A 1790   B 1918   C 1923

6 What do the statements tell you about stars and galaxies?

7 What developments do you think made it possible to discover more about stars and galaxies?

If you could travel at the speed of light (300 000 km per second), this is how long it might take you to reach the following:

Moon	1.3 seconds
Jupiter	35 minutes
Uranus	2.5 hours
Pluto	5 hours

Today, spacecraft can only reach a tiny fraction of the speed of light. For example, *Voyager 2* took over 8 years to reach Uranus. Spacecraft cannot carry enough fuel to run their engines continuously. For most of their journey, thay have to 'coast'. And the speed of light seems to be a universal speed limit. As things approach this speed, it becomes more and more difficult to make them go any faster.

Space distances are sometimes measured in **light years**. A light year is the distance travelled by light in a year. It is nearly 10 million million kilometres. Here are the distances to some of the nearest stars:

Proxima Centauri	**4.3 light years**
Barnard's Star	**5.9 light years**
Sirius	**8.8 light years**
Altair	**16.6 light years**

I have been able to observe distant 'gas clouds' in more detail than ever before. I believe that some of these are not gas clouds at all, but other galaxies beyond our own. The Universe contains millions of galaxies.
Edwin Hubble

My observations suggest that the Sun is towards the edge of the Galaxy, not near its centre. I have studied many tiny 'gas clouds' and think that some of these may be outside the Galaxy.
Harlow Shapley

Some parts of the sky have more stars than others. I think that the Sun must be near the centre of a huge lens-shaped 'island' of stars which I shall call the Galaxy. Among the stars I have seen faint objects that look like tiny gas clouds. But beyond the Galaxy, I believe there is nothing but empty space.
William Herschel

Galaxies

Scientists think that the Sun is one star in a galaxy of over 100 000 million stars. The stars are arranged in huge spiral 'arms' around a central 'hub'. The whole system is slowly rotating and held together by gravitational forces. In the middle picture on the right, you can see a section through our galaxy. The Sun is about 30 000 light years from the galactic centre and takes 225 million years to go round it once. The galaxy in the photograph on the right has a similar structure to our own. Scientists think that there are more than 100 000 million galaxies in the whole Universe.

8 Why do the stars in the galaxy in the photograph look like a bright cloud?

9 In the diagram on the right, use the scale to estimate the distance (in light years) across our galaxy.

10 How long would it take a beam of light to travel right across the galaxy?

11 Make a sketch of our galaxy showing the approximate position of the Sun.

The stars listed in the article on the left are some of the Sun's nearest neighbours.

12 Could you show these stars on your sketch of the galaxy? Explain your answer.

13 From Earth, Sirius looks much brighter than Proxima Centauri. What do you think the reason for this might be?

The expanding Universe

Edwin Hubble analysed the light arriving from distant galaxies. From his measurements, he deduced that the galaxies are speeding away from each other. The Universe is expanding. Scientists have explained Hubble's observations using the **big bang theory**:

About 16 000 million years ago, everything in the Universe existed as a ball of superdense matter and energy no bigger than your fist. This blew up, hurling matter outwards in all directions. The galaxies which formed from this matter have been moving apart ever since, though scientists think that they may be slowing down.

14 What does the big bang theory say is happening to the galaxies?

15 How do you think scientists could have estimated when the big bang occurred?

16 What force could be slowing the galaxies down as they move apart?

There are more than 100 000 million stars in this galaxy

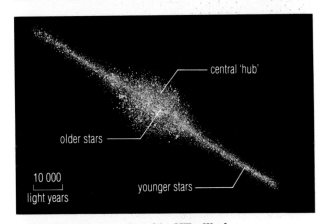

central 'hub'

older stars

10 000
light years

younger stars

Section through our galaxy (the Milky Way)

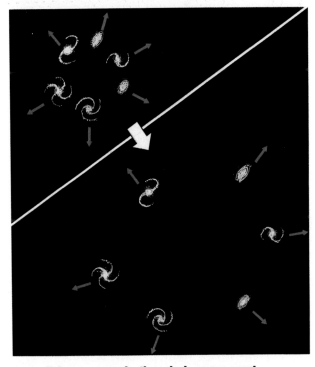

As the Universe expands, the galaxies move apart

O *4.8 Birth and death*

Within galaxies, astronomers have seen new stars starting to form in clouds of gas and dust called **nebulae**. It is likely that our own Sun formed in a swirling nebula about 5000 million years ago. The diagrams on this page show the different stages.

1   A large blob of matter began to form when loose dust and gas were pulled together. What would have pulled them together?

2   As more and more matter rained in on the blob of matter, it heated up. Why?

Deep in the blob of matter, the temperature and pressure eventually became high enough for nuclear reactions to start. The new star (our Sun) started to shine. Around it was a huge, slowly turning disc of left-over gas and dust. This too started to collect into blobs. But these were never big enough for nuclear reactions to start. In time, they began to cool.

3   What do you think the hot blobs of gas and dust around the Sun eventually became?

4   Why did these blobs of matter not form into tiny stars?

Death of a star

The Sun is about half way through its life cycle. At present, it is powered by nuclear reactions in the hydrogen in its core. But that supply of energy will eventually run out. This is what scientists think will happen then:

The nuclear reactions will spread outwards from the core, the core will get even hotter and the Sun will begin to swell. Its outer layer will become so big that it will engulf the Earth. By now, the expansion will have cooled the outer layer to a red glow: the Sun will have become a type of star known as a **red giant**. Eventually, the thin outer layer will drift off into space, exposing a hot, dense core called a **white dwarf**. This tiny star will use helium as its nuclear fuel. When that supply of energy is exhausted, the star will cool and fade for ever.

5   About how long will it be before the Sun completes its life cycle?

6   Draw a series of diagrams following on from the ones on the right, to show what will happen to the Sun in the future.

The Great Nebula in the constellation of Orion

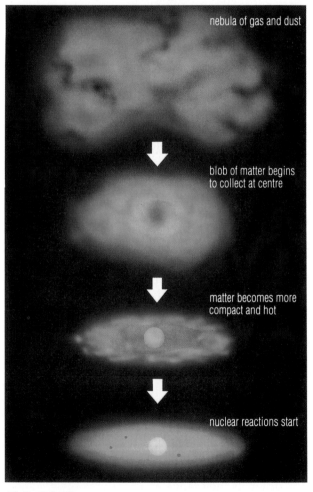

nebula of gas and dust

blob of matter begins to collect at centre

matter becomes more compact and hot

nuclear reactions start

Birth of the Sun

Ideas and beliefs

Over the centuries many ideas have been put forward about the Earth and the Universe. Here are some of them.

Ancient Greek beliefs

The Ancient Greeks believed that the Universe was once a cold mixture which began to move like a whirlpool. In time, matter fell out of this whirlpool to make the Earth. The Sun, Moon and planets were born from the Earth.

Ancient Hindu beliefs

From ancient times, Hindus have believed that the Universe is cyclic. The creator God Shiva controls an endless cycle of birth, destruction and rebirth.

Statue of Shiva

The big crunch?

From their observation of galaxies, scientists think that the Universe is expanding. But the expansion may be slowing down. In billions of years time, the galaxies could start to move towards each other. If so, they will then collide in a big crunch. This might be followed by another big bang .... and so on. Whether all this happens depends partly on the amount of dark matter in the Universe. Dark matter is the name for invisible material which may exist between galaxies. Scientists are still not sure how much dark matter there is. There may be just enough to turn an expanding Universe into a contracting one.

The geocentric (Earth-centred) theory

The Ancient Greeks thought that the Earth was a globe at the centre of the Universe, with the Sun, Moon, planets and stars moving around it. Aristotle (384-322 BC) was able to explain why the Earth's surface must be curved: the Pole Star appeared lower in the sky when viewed in Egypt than it did in Greece. Around 270 BC, Eratosthenes used this idea to calculate the circumference of the Earth. He was accurate to within 80 km.

Heliocentric (Sun-centred) theory

In 1514, Nicholas Copernicus suggested that the Earth was not the centre of the Universe. The Earth and the other planets all moved round the Sun. Copernicus believed that this theory was the only satisfactory way of explaining the motions of the planets. His ideas were taken up by Galileo Galilei (1564-1642), the first astronomer to use a telescope. When Galileo discovered four of Jupiter's moons, he realised that not everything in the sky moved round the Earth. He was persecuted by the Christian Church for suggesting that the Earth was not the centre of the Universe.

With your group...

Here are some questions for you to discuss and answer:

7   In some civilizations, the Sun was worshipped as a god. Why was the Sun believed to be so important?

8   Do you think the Sun is less important to modern industrial civilizations than it was to older ones? Explain your answer.

9   Use drawings to show how the Ancient Greek view of the Solar System compares with our modern one.

10 How do the Ancient Greek and Hindu beliefs about the Universe compare with the modern scientific ideas?

11 See if you can find out what Jews, Christians, Moslems and people of other religions believe about the Universe.

12 If the Universe starts to contract, what force will pull it together?

13 Why may the future of the Universe depend on the amount of dark matter in it?

14 Today, the Christian Church largely supports the work of scientists. Why do you think that the ideas of Copernicus and Galileo were so strongly opposed by the Church at the time?

OXFORD
SCIENCE
programme

P Waves and currents

P 1.1 *Waves everywhere*

In the picture above, many different kinds of waves are producing all sorts of effects. Energy can be moved from one place to another by waves. With your group, see how many kinds of waves you can spot and consider the following questions:

1 What waves can your eyes detect?
2 What invisible waves are in the scene?
3 How do you know the invisible waves are there?
4 What effect does each kind of wave have?
5 What do you think 'energy transfer' means? What energy transfers by waves can you find in the picture?

Investigating ripples

If drips from an overhanging tree hit the surface of a pond, ripples (small waves) spread outwards across the water. With your group, discuss and answer the following:

6 Like all materials, water is made up of tiny particles. What happens to the particles in the water when waves pass? Do they move outwards like the waves, do they go up and down, or do they move in some other way?

■ Design and carry out an experiment to find out what happens to the particles in water when ripples travel across it. Then prepare a report on what you have found.

Useful information
• A small floating object might behave like one of the water particles.

Electromagnetic waves

In previous work, you may have come across a family of waves called the **electromagnetic spectrum**. You may also know something about the different effects they can have. To help you check your ideas, look at the information on the right. Names of waves and their effects have been muddled up. And one of the types of wave isn't a member of the electromagnetic family at all!

7 Decide which type of wave is the odd one out.

8 Draw a table showing the different types of electromagnetic waves and their effects. Remember to
   • decide in which order you will list the waves.
   • make sure that each wave is paired with the correct effect.
   • see if you can add any more effects to your table.

Investigating sound waves

Sound waves can be detected by a microphone. If this is linked to a CRO (cathode ray oscilloscope) you can see a trace called a **waveform** on the screen. However, when you look at the waveform you aren't seeing the waves themselves. You are looking at a graph which shows how the air pressure near the microphone rises and falls with time.

Use an oscilloscope connected to a microphone to find out what types of waveform are given by different sounds.

Things to think about
• What sort of sounds are you going to investigate?
• What sources will you need?

What to do
■ Find out from your teacher how the microphone should be connected to the CRO.
■ Carry out your tests. Draw the different waveforms you observe.
■ Find out what happens to the waveform if a sound becomes louder.
■ Find out what happens to the waveform if a sound becomes higher in pitch.

9 Try matching the waveforms shown on the right with the different sounds in the pictures next to them.

P 1.2 Waves on the move

The pictures on the right show different things happening to water waves. With your group, decide what you think is happening in each one and consider the following questions:

1 In the top picture (**A**), what is happening to the ripples as they hit the log?

2 Are the ripples always the same distance apart?

3 What else have you studied that changes direction like the waves shown here?

4 When is this change of direction useful?

The change of direction of these waves is an example of **reflection**.

In the middle picture (**B**), the ripples are moving from a deeper region into a shallower region.

5 Look at the separation of the wave crests. Does it stay the same or change when the waves pass from deeper to shallower water?

6 What happens to the direction of the waves when they get to the shallower water?

Scientists call this type of change of direction **refraction**.

7 Where else have you studied refraction?

8 What sort of waves were refracting then?

9 When is refraction useful?

When water waves are travelling along, their up and down movements keep happening at the same, steady rate.

10 If the wave crests suddenly get closer together, what does this tell you about the speed of the waves?

11 What do you think happens to the speed of water waves when they travel from a deeper region to a shallower region?

The bottom picture (**C**) shows much larger water waves. These are entering a harbour.

12 What is happening to the waves as they enter the harbour?

13 Are the wave crests the same distance apart after entering the harbour? What does your answer tell you about the speed of the waves?

14 What energy changes are occuring when the waves enter the harbour?

Scientists call this spreading out of waves **diffraction**.

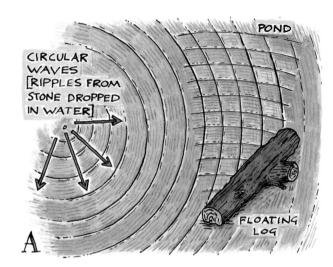

POND

CIRCULAR WAVES [RIPPLES FROM STONE DROPPED IN WATER]

FLOATING LOG

A

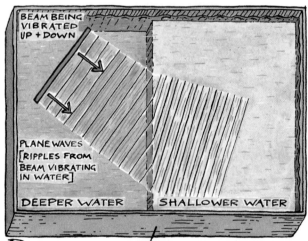

BEAM BEING VIBRATED UP + DOWN

PLANE WAVES [RIPPLES FROM BEAM VIBRATING IN WATER]

DEEPER WATER

SHALLOWER WATER

B

TANK

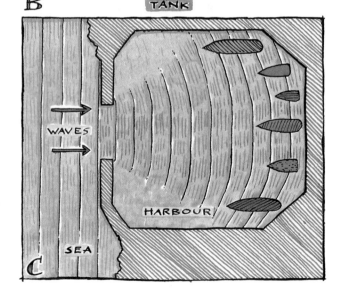

WAVES

HARBOUR

SEA

C

Plane and circular

Some of the waves on the opposite page have been labelled as either **plane waves** or **circular waves**.

15 Explain what you think the difference is between plane waves and circular waves.

16 Which of these two types is moving towards the harbour entrance?

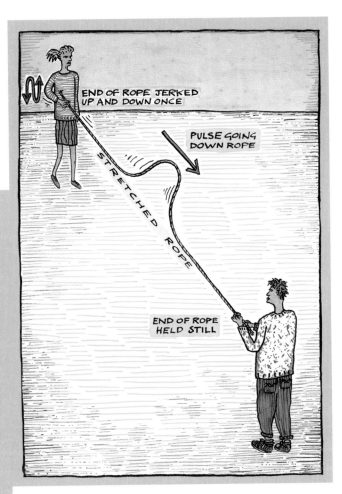

Strings and ropes

Some students noticed that strings on instruments like the guitar vibrated when plucked. They reckoned that waves travelling up and down the strings were making the vibrations. They argued about what would happen if they sent a single wave pulse along a rope which was held tight at both ends. One student thought that the wave pulse would reflect (bounce back) when it reached the far end. Another thought it would stop.

Find out what happens when waves travel down a long rope (or length of tubing).

What to do

- Hold the rope as in the diagram on the right. It should be stretched, but not too tight.
- The person at the far end should keep that end still. The other person should send a single pulse down the rope by jerking the end up and down once.
- What happens when the wave reaches the far end? Does anything else happen after that?
- Now try sending lots of waves down the rope one after the other.
- What happens if the person sending the waves moves their hand up and down more quickly or more slowly?
- By changing the speed of your hand movements, see if you can get waves in the rope to combine so that they look as though they are standing still.
- Write a report on all you have found out.

Combined dangers

Sometimes, waves can combine to cause huge vibrations. In 1940, high winds made the roadway of the Tacoma Bridge, USA, behave like a stretched rope with waves travelling along it. The vibrations destroyed the bridge. Nowadays, bridge models are tested in wind tunnels to make sure that this cannot happen.

Tacoma Bridge, USA

P 1.3 Waves and ripples

Look at the diagram and the panel of information on the right. They show some of the terms which can be used to describe waves.

1 What is the distance between one crest and the next called?
2 What is the distance between one trough and the next called?
3 What is the height of a crest above the average level called?
4 What unit is used to measure wavelength?
5 If waves have a 'frequency of 2 Hz', what does this mean?
6 How do you make waves of a higher frequency?
7 If waves have a 'frequency of 2 kHz', what does this mean?

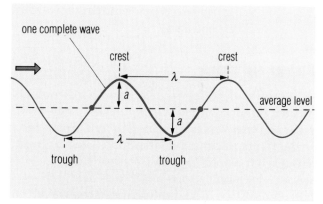

a = **amplitude** *(measured in metres)*
λ = **wavelength** *(measured in metres)*
(λ **is the Greek letter 'lamda')**

The number of complete waves sent out every second is called the **frequency** of the waves.

Frequency is measured in **hertz (Hz)**.
1 Hz means 1 complete wave every second.

1 kHz (kilohertz) = 1000 Hz
1 MHz (megahertz) = 1 000 000 Hz

Investigating water waves

Water waves can reflect, refract and diffract under different conditions. There are two sorts of water waves: plane waves and circular waves.

■ Design and carry out your own investigation to produce plane and circular water waves and study their behaviour. The waves will be ripples on water. You will need a large bowl (or deep tray), and items chosen by you.

Things to think about
• How can you make circular waves?
• How can you make plane waves?
• How will you make the waves reflect?
• How will you make the waves refract?
• How will you make the waves diffract?
• Why could it be a problem if the waves reflect from the sides of the bowl?

Using a ripple tank

A ripple tank is a piece of equipment specially designed for studying the behaviour of waves. The waves used are tiny ripples on water. You can see one type of ripple tank in the diagram on the right. The tank has sloping sides so that waves are not reflected from the sides. The water has a lamp above it so that shadows of the ripples can be seen on the sheet of paper underneath.

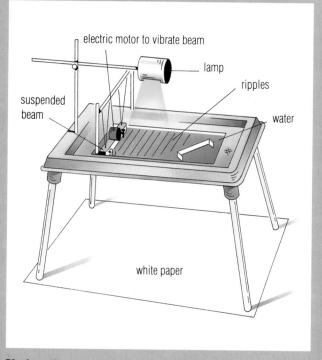

Ripple tank

With a ripple tank, an electric motor is used to vibrate a suspended beam. The beam can be adjusted so that it just dips into the water. Or it can be raised and a pointer fixed to it so that this dips into the water. Depending on the arrangement used, you can produce circular waves or plane waves.

8   What type of waves do you think are produced if the beam is dipping in the water?

9   What type of waves are produced if the pointer is dipping in the water?

Use a ripple tank to investigate plane waves and circular waves. Find out how the frequency affects the wavelength. Investigate the effects of putting different barriers and shapes in the water.

You need

Ripple tank, variable low voltage power supply for motor, low voltage power supply for bulb, connecting leads, beaker, water, different barriers and shapes to put in the ripple tank. (You can see some of these in the diagram at the top of the next column.)

Safety

• *Make sure that power supplies have maximum voltages which do not exceed those needed by the motor and the bulb.*

• *Do not attempt to move the ripple tank when it has water in it.*

Useful information

• The depth of the water can affect the quality of the ripple shadows. So can the depth of the beam or pointer in the water.

• The ripples may be easier to see if a drop of washing-up liquid is added to the water.

• It is useful to make sketches of what you observe each time you use the ripple tank.

• By using a stroboscope instead of an ordinary lamp, and flashing it at the right rate, you can make the ripples appear to stand still. But this is difficult to do!

What to do

■   Set up the ripple tank to get the best possible plane waves.

■   Vary the frequency of the waves by varying the speed of the motor.

■   What happens to the wavelength if the frequency goes up?

■   What happens to the wavelength if the frequency goes down?

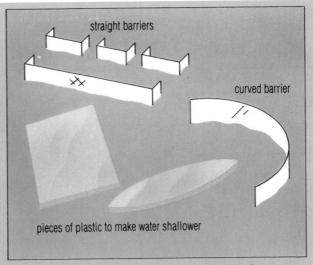

Barriers and shapes you could use in a ripple tank

More things to do

■   Investigate the reflection of plane waves at a straight barrier. Find out what happens if the barrier is at an angle to the waves, as in the diagram of the ripple tank.

■   Investigate the reflection of plane waves at a curved barrier.

■   Find out what happens when circular waves are reflected by different barriers.

■   Make part of the water in the tank very shallow by putting in a thin plastic shape. See if you can observe the refraction of plane waves. (This is a tricky one to set up!)

■   Try sending plane waves through a gap between two straight barriers.

■   See what happens if you change the size of the gap to about the same size as the wavelength of the waves. When do the water waves diffract the most?

■   Try passing plane waves through *two* gaps close together, as shown below. See what pattern this produces.

■   Write a report on what you have found out from all your investigations.

P 1.4 Vibrations and waves

Investigating springs

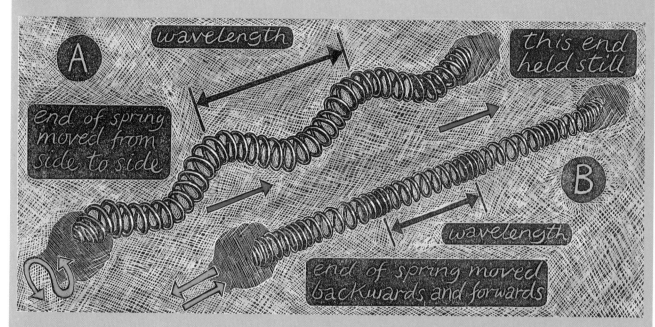

Some students had investigated waves travelling along ropes and across water. They decided to find out if waves could travel along a stretched Slinky spring. You can see how they held the spring in the diagram above. They reckoned that the person sending the waves could make the spring vibrate in two different ways: first, by moving their hand from side to side (**A**); second by moving their hand backwards and forwards (**B**). This meant that two completely different types of wave could be sent along the spring.

Investigate a slinky spring for yourself:

- Try sending different types of wave along the spring. What happens to the waves when they reach the far end?
- Find out what changes are needed to make the waves travel faster or slower.
- Try studying the movement of a single coil very carefully:
  Watch what happens to a coil when the two different types of wave pass.
  Draw diagrams to show what you found.

Caution!
Be careful not to overstretch the Slinky spring or tangle it.

When the direction of vibration is at right angles to the direction the waves are travelling, the waves are known as **transverse waves**. Waves with side-to-side vibrations are like this. So are waves with up-and-down vibrations.

When the direction of vibration is in the same direction as the waves are travelling, the waves are known as **longitudinal waves**.

1 Look at examples **A** and **B** in the diagram above. Which one shows the longitudinal waves and which the transverse waves?
2 Which of these two types do you think water waves are?
3 Longitudinal waves are sometimes called **compression** waves. Why do you think this is?

Compressions and rarefactions

In a longitudinal wave, regions where the coils (or other particles) are pushed closer together are called **compressions**. Regions where they are pulled further apart are called **rarefactions**.

4 Draw your own version of example **B** in the diagram above. Mark on the compressions and rarefactions.

Speed, frequency and wavelength

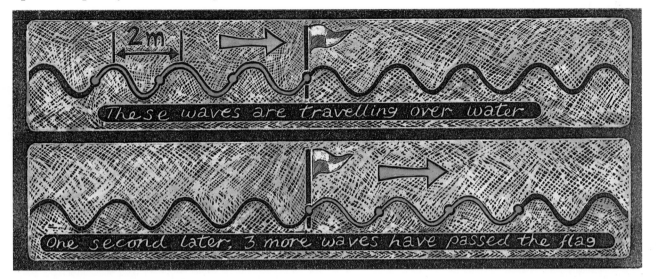

These waves are travelling over water

One second later, 3 more waves have passed the flag

The top part of the diagram above shows some waves travelling across water. The bottom part shows the same situation one second later. So you can see how far waves have travelled in one second. Use the information given in the diagram to help you answer the following:

5 What is the *frequency* of the waves in Hz?
6 What is the *wavelength* of the waves in metres?
7 How far does each wave travel in one second?
8 What is the *speed* of the waves in metres per second (m/s)?

Scientists have worked out an equation linking speed, frequency and wavelength:

speed = frequency x wavelength

In questions **5** and **6**, you wrote down the frequency and the wavelength of the waves.

9 Use these answers in the above equation to calculate the speed of the waves. Does your answer agree with the one you worked out for question **8**?
10 Imagine that the speed of the waves stays the same, but the frequency is increased. What do you think will happen to the wavelength? Will it be *longer* or *shorter* than before? To answer this question, think back to the results of your ripple tank investigations in the previous spread.
11 Imagine that the speed of the waves stays the same, but there are now *six* waves every second instead of three. Use the equation to calculate the new wavelength. Is it shorter or longer than before?

Resonance

It had been a long, tiring day, and I could hardly keep my eyes open. Once on the bus, I settled into my seat and tried to sleep with my head resting against a side window. But every time the bus pulled into a bus stop, the window started vibrating so much that it woke me up! The engine seemed to be the source of the vibration. When it was revving fast, there was no problem. But when it was just ticking over, it set the whole side of the bus in motion. Later, my science teacher told me that this was an example of **resonance**. The side of the bus had a frequency at which it would naturally vibrate, rather like a guitar string. If the engine vibrations matched this natural frequency, the vibrations would build up.

The report above was written by a student who had travelled home from school by bus.

12 What was making the side windows of the bus vibrate?
13 When were the vibrations at their greatest?
14 What was the effect called?
15 Look back through the previous spreads in this module. Can you find any other examples where large vibrations were set off by something else? In each case, say what the source of the vibration was, and what was made to vibrate as a result.

1.5 Sending sounds

The instruments in the picture are giving many different sounds. In every case however, the sound waves are being produced by something vibrating. The sound waves are longitudinal waves which travel out through the air. They carry energy from one place to another. With your group:

1 Make a list of musical instruments, including those you can see in the picture.
2 Which of the instruments produce mainly high notes?
3 Which of the instruments produce mainly low notes?
4 For each instrument, try to decide what is being vibrated to start the sound wave off.
5 How are the sound waves detected?
6 In the diagram on the right, what happens to the molecules in the air just above the drum when the drumskin moves downwards?
7 What happens to the molecules in the air just above the drum when the drumskin moves upwards?
8 What do you think happens to molecules in the air a few metres away from the drum when the sound waves pass?
9 Draw a sketch showing how you think the sound waves will move from the drum as it is played.

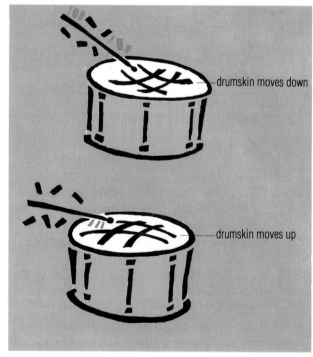

10 What energy changes take place from just before the drumskin is hit to the time when the sound is detected?
11 What vibrates when you sing or talk?
12 What other waves have you investigated that are longitudinal waves?

80

To answer some of the questions on this page you may need to plan and carry out investigations with your group.

Loud notes

If you hold a vibrating tuning fork next to your ear you can hear a clear note of a certain frequency but it is not very loud.

13 How could you make the note louder?

14 The diagram on the right shows a vibrating tuning fork. What do you think is meant by the **amplitude** of vibration of the tuning fork. What happens to the loudness if this amplitude is increased?

15 What happens to the loudness if you stand a vibrating tuning fork on a table? Why do you think this happens?

16 How are instruments in an orchestra able to produce such loud notes?

17 How are instruments in a rock band able to produce such loud notes?

High and low

When people talk about high or low notes, they say that the notes have a high or low **pitch**. The pitch depends on the frequency of vibration of the sound source.

18 What happens to the pitch if the frequency goes up? To help you answer this question, you could listen to the sounds from tuning forks of different frequencies.

19 If a stretched string, wire or rubber band is vibrating, what affects the pitch of the sound produced? To help you answer this question you could carry out tests on stretched rubber bands of different lengths and thicknesses. Remember: when you carry out your tests, you must first decide what to keep the same, and what to change, each time.

Frequency ranges

Different animals produce and hear sounds of different frequency ranges. As you grow older, your hearing range decreases. You can probably hear a much wider range of frequencies than your teacher! People with hearing difficulties may hear sounds in a limited range of frequencies only. Look at the data in the table on this page.

20 Present the data in the form of a chart or graph. You could use bars to show the different frequency ranges.

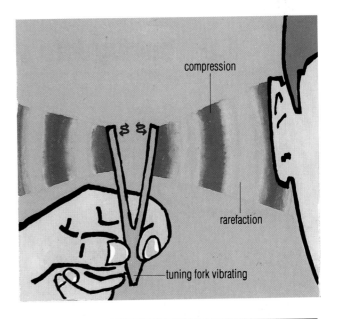

Animal	Frequency range in Hz	
	Sounds produced	Sounds heard
human	500 to 2500	50 to 20 000
dog	500 to 4000	500 to 50 000
cat	500 to 5000	500 to 66 000
porpoise	8000 to 120 000	2500 to 130 000
grasshopper	8000 to 100 000	2500 to 18 000
bat	12 000 to 120 000	1500 to 120 000

21 Which animals can hear a larger range of frequencies than they can produce?

22 What is the largest frequency range produced by any of the animals shown?

23 Which animal cannot hear some of the sounds it produces?

24 How might you measure your own hearing frequency range?

1.6 Looking into sound waves

Sound waves in air

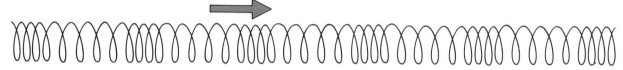

Longitudinal waves in Slinky spring

Sound waves are longitudinal waves, so they behave rather like longitudinal waves in a Slinky spring. The diagram above shows longitudinal waves in a Slinky spring and in air. The waves in air have been drawn as a series of lines.

1 What material is each set of waves passing through?

2 How do the coils of the spring move when the waves pass?

3 How does the air move when the sound waves pass?

4 Draw your own version of the diagrams. Mark in one wavelength on each set of waves. Label any compressions and rarefactions.

Stopping the sound

A double glazing company wonders whether their windows would stop all sounds if there was no air at all between the two layers of glass. They think that sound waves must have a solid, liquid or gas to travel through, and cannot pass through a vacuum (completely empty space).

- Investigate their idea. Find out if sound waves cannot pass through a vacuum.
- Design experiments to find out if sound waves can travel through solids and liquids.

You need
Equipment on the right, items chosen by you.

Now answer these questions:

5 What happened to the sound when the air was pumped out of the jar?

6 Why was it better to have the electric bell suspended in the jar, rather than resting on the bottom?

7 Double glazed windows normally have air, not a vacuum, between the glass layers. Why do you think a vacuum is not used?

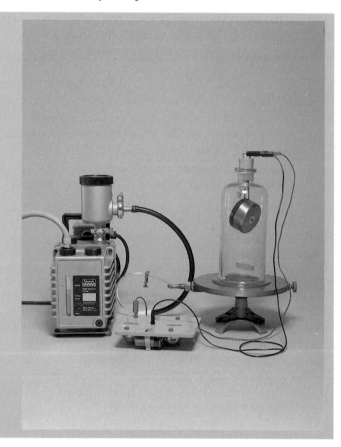

Making music

Different types of musical instrument can sound very different even when the same note is played on them.

If a microphone is connected to it, an oscilloscope can be used to study the sounds from different instruments. The sounds are shown as transverse waveforms on the screen. These give information about the frequency and amplitude of the sound waves reaching the microphone.

8　When Mike looked at a waveform on an oscilloscope, he said: 'That proves that sound waves are really transverse waves, not longitudinal ones'. What answer would you give him?

■　Using an oscilloscope and a microphone, compare the waveforms produced by different musical instruments. Do this when the instruments are sounding different notes and also when they are sounding the same note. Sketch any waveforms you observe and label them.

More waveforms

On the right, you can see some examples of waveforms obtained by some students who were investigating tuning forks.

First, compare waveforms A and B:

9　Which has the higher amplitude?
10　How do the frequencies compare?
11　If you could hear sounds A and B, how would the sounds compare?

Now compare waveforms C and D:

12　How do the amplitudes compare?
13　Which has the higher frequency?
14　If you could hear sounds C and D, how would the sounds compare?

When the students looked at the waveforms from a violin and a piano they saw more complex patterns. Like other instruments, these instruments produce sounds which have higher frequencies, called **harmonics** mixed in with the basic note. It is the harmonics which help give each type of instrument its characteristic sound. Scientists say that the different sounds have a different **quality**.

15　Synthesizers work electronically. They can be made to sound like a whole range of different instruments. How do you think these different sounds are produced?

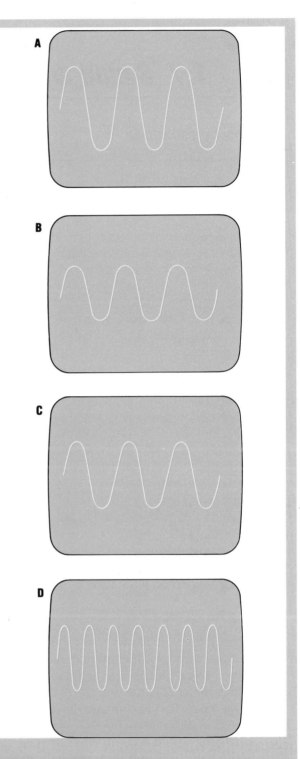

A

B

C

D

Making a musical instrument

Try designing and making a musical instrument using simple equipment. It could be stringed, wind or percussion!

■　Make a list of the things you will need.
■　Sketch your design.
■　Consider how you will tune your musical instrument and what you might play.
■　Make and test your instrument.

P 1.7 Sound waves in action

Listening for reflections

Blind people can use sound waves to help them tell how near they are to buildings.

1 How can a blind person use a stick to sense the position of objects?

Find out if sound waves reflect like other waves. Do this by carrying out an experiment like the one shown in the diagram on the right.

You need
Two tubes (e.g. cardboard), source of quiet noise (such as ticking clock), sheet of hardboard (or glass), protractor.

What to do
- Set up the equipment, but without the hardboard in position. Check that you cannot hear the noise. Why is this check important?
- Now put the hardboard in position. Alter its angle to see if you can detect a noise. Is there a best position for this? If so, measure the angles *i* and *r*.
- What do you notice about angles *i* and *r*?
- Investigate with the tubes at other angles.
- What other waves reflect like this?
- What are reflected sounds called?
- Make a report on what you have found out.

Waiting for waves

The table on the right shows how fast sound waves travel through different materials.

2 Why is there a blank next to a 'vacuum'?
3 Which material lets sound travel the fastest?
4 Draw a bar chart to compare the different speeds in different materials.
5 How long would it take a whale to hear an underwater call from another whale 3000 metres away?
6 How long (to the nearest second) would it take you to hear a sound which came from 1000 metres away?
7 If your shout was reflected from a cliff 660 metres away, how long would it be before you heard the echo?
8 Why does singing in the bathroom sound different from singing in the bedroom?

Material	Speed of sound in m/s
vacuum	-
air	330
water	1500
brick	3600
iron	5100
aluminium	5100
glass	6000

Underwater listener

84

Echo sounding

Ships can use equipment called **sonar** to check the depth of water beneath them. A pulse of sound is sent downwards. It reflects from the sea bed. The time for the pulse to travel down and back is measured.

Suppose it takes 2 seconds for a pulse to reach the sea bed and return:

9 If the speed of sound in water is 1500 metres per second, how far will the sound have travelled in 2 seconds.

10 In this time, the sound will have travelled to the sea bed *and back again*. So what is the depth of water under the ship?

Now suppose it only takes 1 second for a pulse to reach the sea bed and return:

11 What is the depth of water under the ship this time?

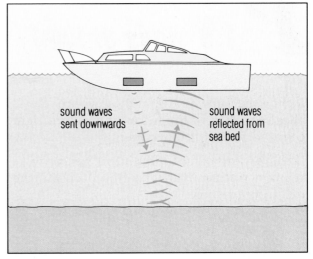

Echo sounding: the deeper the water, the longer it takes pulses of sound to travel to the bottom and reflect back.

Heard but not seen

In the picture on the right, Alison can hear her father even though he is out of sight.

12 What has happened to the sound waves?

13 Where else have you seen waves behaving like this?

14 What is the effect called?

■ Try sending sound in one particular direction and seeing how much the waves spread out. Before you do this decide on the following:
  • How will you send the sound in one direction to start with?
  • How will you detect the sound?

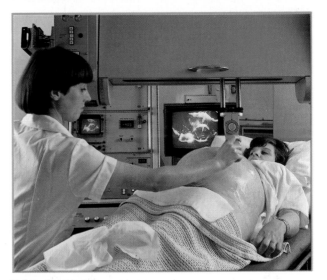

Using ultrasound

Ultrasound is the name for sounds whose frequencies are above the range of human hearing. One use of ultrasound is to check the development of a baby in its mother's womb. This is what is happening in the photograph on the right. An ultrasound transmitter is moved over the mother's body. A detector picks up sound waves which are reflected from different layers of tissue. The signals are processed by a computer which puts an image on a screen.

15 What device will the detector contain to change the reflected sound waves into electrical signals?

16 When doctors need to see an image of the baby, why is it safer for them to use ultrasound than to take an X-ray photograph?

Using ultrasound

P 1.8 Rays of light

Light is the name we use for those electro-magnetic waves which our eyes can detect. Light comes in many different colours.

From very early times, the rainbow has been a source of wonder. With your group, consider the following questions.
1 What superstitions do you know about rainbows?
2 What can rainbows tell you about the weather?
3 How do you think rainbows are made?
4 Where else do you see the colours of rainbows apart from in the sky?
5 How do you think you might create a rainbow in the laboratory?

Investigating a spectrum

The range of colours in the rainbow is called a **spectrum**. See if you can create a spectrum in the laboratory using a prism and a beam of white light.

You need
Prism, ray box with single slit, low voltage power supply, sheet of white paper, pencil and ruler, darkened laboratory.

Useful information
• White light is a mixture of waves of different frequencies. If these are separated out, we see them as different colours.
• Glass or clear plastic slows light waves, rather like shallow water slows water waves. This makes the waves **refract** (bend).
• Different colours are slowed different amounts by glass or clear plastic. The more the light is slowed, the more it is bent.
• The spreading of the colours by a prism is called **dispersion**.

Did you know?

Most people think they can see six or seven colours in the spectrum. But really, there are millions of colours in a steady change from one end to the other.

What to do
■ Use the raybox and the slit to produce a narrow beam of white light.
■ Place the prism on the paper and shine the beam through the prism.
■ Turn the prism until you find a position that gives you a clear spectrum.
■ By drawing round the prism and marking in all the rays, make a careful record of your spectrum. Remember to mark all the colours and their positions.

Answer these with your group:
6 What colours did you see in the spectrum?
7 Which colour was refracted most by the prism?
8 Which colour was refracted least?
9 Why are the different colours in white light spread into a spectrum?
10 Which of the colours travels slowest through a prism?

This sentence is useful for remembering the main colours of the spectrum: 'Richard Of York Gave Battle In Vain'. The first letter of each word is the first letter of a colour.
11 What colours do the letters stand for?

Optical fibres

Optical fibres are thin strands of glass which light can pass through. In a telephone system, they can be used to carry signals. Sound vibrations are used to 'pulsate' the light from a tiny laser at one end of the fibre. At the other end, the light pulsations are detected by electronic equipment, changed into electrical signals and then into sound. Optical fibres can be arranged together in a bundle to form a cable.

■ Try passing light from a raybox along an optical fibre (or flexible plastic rod). Find out if the light always reaches the end even if the fibre is bent.

Cables containing optical fibres can be bent to make light go round corners.

12 Apart from communications, can you think of any other uses for optical fibres in cables?

Reflection or refraction?

Two students were arguing about how the light waves stayed inside an optical fibre. Nikki reckoned that the sides of the glass must be reflecting the light. Jo didn't think that this was possible because the light would refract through the sides and escape.

Find out if glass can be used to reflect light without any light escaping by refraction.

You need
Semicircular glass or plastic block, sheet of white paper, raybox, slit, low voltage power pack, protractor, pencil and ruler, darkened laboratory.

Useful information
• Using a semicircular glass or plastic block as shown on the right you can direct a ray at the flat, inside face of the block at any angle you like.

What to do
■ Set up the experiment.
■ Find out what happens to the ray as you change the angle *i* in the diagram.
■ Make a record of any block and ray positions you try out.
■ What happens as you increase the angle *i*? Make a report on what you have found out.

13 How do *you* think light travels along an optical fibre?

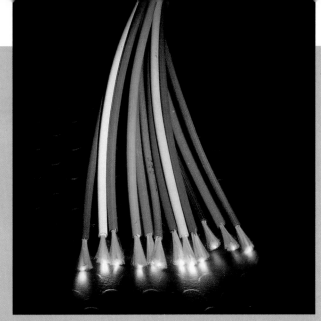

Optical fibres

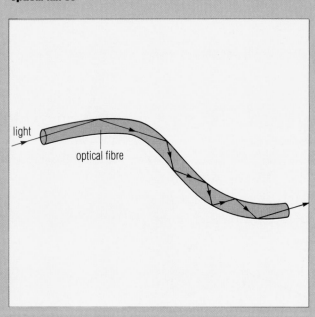

Nikki's idea

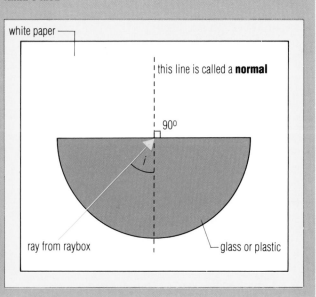

P 1.9 *Investigating lenses*

Lenses refract light, but in a rather special way. They change the direction of light rays so that you can see an **image**.

1   List as many things as you can which contain lenses.
2   Which ones give an image which is smaller than real life?
3   Which ones give an image which is larger than real life?

In this spread, you will be investigating the images formed by convex lenses.

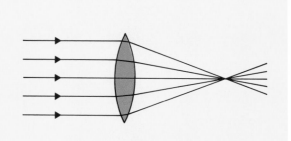

Comparing images

A student was investigating how a convex lens could form an image of a distant window on a screen. You can see his experimental arrangement above. He adjusted the position of the lens until there was a clear image on the screen: the image was in **focus**.

Carry out the investigation yourself, starting with a thick convex lens. Find out the answers to these questions:

■   Which way up is the image?
■   What is the distance from the lens to the screen when the image is in focus?
■   If you change the thin convex lens for a thicker one, which way must you move the screen to keep the image in focus?
■   What is the distance from the lens to the screen now?
■   How has the size of the image changed?

The diagram above shows how a convex lens focuses light rays from a distant point, such as a point on a window. The rays come to a focus at a point called the **principal focus**. The distance from the lens to the image is called the **focal length** of the lens.

4   Which convex lens has the longer focal length, a thick one or a thin one?
5   Draw your own version of the diagram. Label the *principal focus* and the *focal length*.
6   Draw the diagram again, only this time showing a thinner lens.
7   What were the focal lengths of the two lenses you used in your investigation?

A camera uses a convex lens to form an image on a piece of film at the back.

8   If you could alter the design of a camera, what changes would you make so that the image on the film was bigger?

Bigger and bigger

card with square hole cut in middle

tracing paper stuck over hole

picture on tracing paper

raybox

convex lens in holder

metre rule

white card screen

Another student had an idea for a model projector. You can see the arrangement she used above. Try it for yourself:

■ Put the slide and the screen exactly one metre apart.

■ Move the lens backwards and forward between the slide and the screen. How many positions can you find which give a clearly focused image on the screen?

■ Choose a position which gives a large image. Which way up is this image?

■ Now see if you can make a bigger image. You are allowed to move the screen and the slide (with its raybox), but not the lens! What changes did you have to make?

■ If you were designing a projector to give the largest possible image in a small room, would you use a thick lens or a thin one? Find out by investigation.

Investigating magnifiers

Convex lenses are not always used for forming images on screens. Sometimes, they are put close to something to make it look bigger. A lens used like this is often called a **magnifier** or **magnifying glass**.

■ Investigate which magnifier gives the best magnification: a thick lens or a thin lens.

Image in the eye

The human eye contains a convex lens system. You can see this in the diagram below.

9 Which part of the eye acts as a screen for the image?

10 Which way up is the image?

11 List ways in which the eye is *similar* to a camera and ways in which it is *different*. To answer this question, you may have to find more information in reference books.

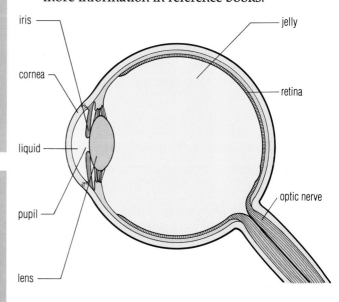

iris

jelly

cornea

retina

liquid

pupil

optic nerve

lens

P 1.10 More wave investigations

Sometimes, wavy patterns may appear on television pictures, or the sound from a radio can go crackly or fade away. When this happens, an announcer may apologize for the **interference**. Interference is the name which scientists use to describe the result of two (or more) sets of waves becoming mixed up.

1 What causes interference on TV or radio?

Interference can happen with light waves as well as radio waves. You will be investigating the interference of two sets of light waves on the opposite page. But first, start by taking a closer look at diffraction.

Light waves diffracting

When water waves pass through a narrow gap, they **diffract** (spread out).

2 Think back to your ripple tank experiments. For the greatest diffraction, how must the size of the gap compare with the wavelength of the waves?

A student wondered whether light waves might diffract like water waves. However, he had read that light waves have very small wavelengths.

3 See if you can find out a typical wavelength for light waves. You may be able to find the information in this book!

4 If light waves are to be diffracted, why might a very narrow gap be needed for this?

Now investigate whether light waves are diffracted by a very narrow slit.

You need
Raybox with a vertical filament bulb, very narrow single slit, low voltage supply, white screen, darkened laboratory.

What to do
- Arrange the raybox and slit in front of the screen as shown in the diagram in the next column. Check that the screen only gets light from the slit.
- Look at the screen. Make a report on what you observe. What do your observations show?

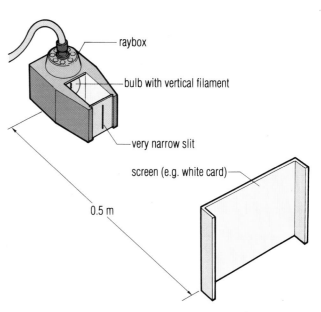

Particles or waves?

Isaac Newton (1642-1727) thought that light rays were streams of tiny particles. Thomas Young (1773-1829) argued that light travelled as waves. The next experiment on the opposite page was first performed by Young in 1801.

5 How do you think Young and Newton would each have explained the results of your last experiment?

Light waves interfering

Another student remembered that when water waves interfere they sometimes cancel each other out so that the water is flat. This is called **destructive interference**. At other times, waves can add together to give bigger waves. This is called **constructive interference**. She wondered what might happen if light waves interfered.

6   What do you think you might see if there was destructive interference between two sets of light waves?

Now find out if two diffracted sets of light waves interfere.

You need
Raybox with a vertical filament bulb, low voltage power supply, tracing-paper screen, two very narrow slits close together on a slide, coloured filters, darkened laboratory.

What to do
- Set up your experiment as in the diagram on the right. Make sure that only light from the double slit falls on the screen.
- Look at the screen. Can you see dark lines? Can you see bright lines with coloured edges? All these lines are called interference fringes.
- Which fringes do you think are due to constructive interference?
- Which fringes do you think are due to destructive interference?
- Put a red filter in front of the slits. What effect does this have on the fringes? Does the distance between them change?
- Repeat the last step but, this time, use a blue filter.
- The closer together the fringes, the shorter the wavelength of the light. What do your observations tell you about the wavelengths of red and blue light?

Investigating microwaves

The transmitter in the diagram on the right gives microwaves with a wavelength of 3 cm. Microwaves are invisible, but you can use a detector connected to a meter to find out where they are.

- Using the equipment shown, investigate whether microwaves can pass through metal. Then investigate the diffraction and interference of microwaves.

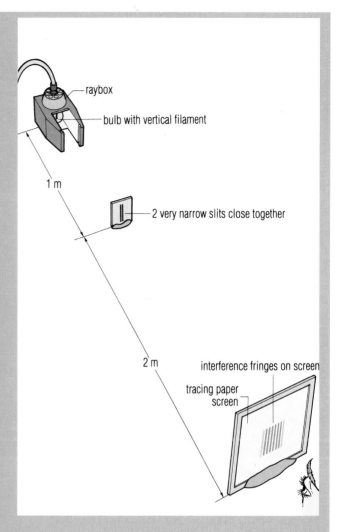

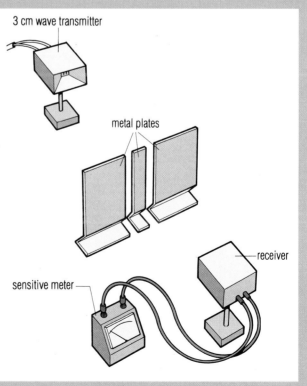

91

P 1.11 Electromagnetic waves at work

The table below shows the different types of electromagnetic waves. All are transverse waves which travel through empty space at a speed of approximately 300 000km/s.

1 How far will electromagnetic waves travel through empty space in one second?

2 Are electromagnetic waves *transverse* or *longitudinal*?

3 Which waves have the longest wavelength?

4 Which waves have the highest frequency?

5 Which waves in the visible range have the shortest wavelength?

6 Which waves are used for long-distance communications?

7 What would you feel if your hands absorbed infrared waves?

8 Which waves can be detected by photographic film?

9 Make a large chart of the different electromagnetic waves:

- Start by drawing a long line along the middle of the chart. This will be your wavelength scale.
- Next to the line, write in the different types of waves in order of increasing wavelength. The wavelengths do not need to be marked out to scale.
- Write in some examples of where the different types of waves come from.
- Write in as many different uses of the waves as you can find out about.

Sending signals by radio

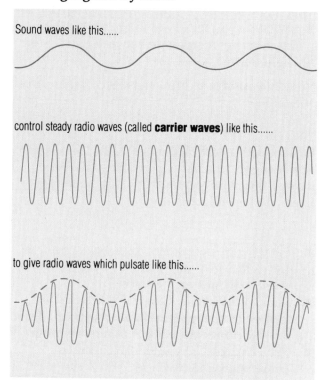

Sound waves like this......

control steady radio waves (called **carrier waves**) like this......

to give radio waves which pulsate like this......

Before speech or music can be broadcast, the sound waves must be changed into electrical signals. In the transmitter, these signals are used to vary the radio waves sent out, so that they 'pulsate' in the same way as the original sound vibrations. The diagram above shows one way of doing this. It is called **amplitude modulation.**

	Type of waves	Typical wavelength	Example of source	Example of detector
low frequency ↑	radio waves	LW 1500 m UHF 1 m	transmitting aerial	receiving aerial
	microwaves	1 cm		
	infrared	0.01 mm	electric fire	infrared camera
	light	red 0.000 7 mm violet 0.000 4 mm	Sun	eye
	ultraviolet	0.000 1 mm	mercury lamp	photographic film
	X-rays	0.000 001 mm	X-ray tube	geiger counter
high frequency ↓	gamma rays	0.000 000 1 mm	radioactive material	

At the receiver, the pulsating radio waves are used to produce a tiny, pulsating current. This is **amplified** (made bigger) and passed through a loudspeaker so that it sends out a copy of the original sound waves.

10 What device changes sounds into electrical signals?

11 In amplitude modulation, what feature of the radio waves is altered by the modulating signal?

12 Why must the signals be amplified at the radio receiver?

Microwaves can also be used for sending signals. Sound, picture and data signals are sent to and from satellites using microwaves.

13 If some microwaves have a wavelength of 0.1 metres, what is their frequency? (To answer this, you will need to remember, or look up, the link between speed, frequency and wavelength.)

Microwave ovens

The microwaves in a microwave oven are produced by an electronic device called a **magnetron**. The waves are normally transmitted into the oven from the top. Any food which absorbs their energy heats up.

14 Why do you think a microwave oven might have cold spots?

15 How do different manufacturers try to overcome the problem?

16 What electromagnetic waves are used in an ordinary oven? Compared with an ordinary oven, what are the advantages and disadvantages of using a microwave oven.

Ultraviolet and infrared lamps

Ultraviolet lamps are used over sunbeds to help people get a tan. These beds are less popular than they used to be and should only be used with great care.

17 What is the problem with ultraviolet radiation?

18 Why is the problem getting worse?

Infrared lamps can be a great help in treating muscular pain such as backache, but they have very strict safety instructions.

19 Why do you have to be careful when using an infrared lamp?

20 Why, for safety, is it important to check both the exposure time and the distance from the lamp?

Mystery rays

Mystery rays near airfield

At the time, there were reports of strange happenings at the military airfield. Locals claimed that dead seagulls had been found near the strange transmitting aerials, and that they showed every sign of having been cooked. Many believed that top-secret mystery rays were responsible. It was rumoured that the invisible rays were microwaves which could be reflected by metals and were being used to detect enemy aircraft over fifty miles from the coast. But it was not safe to debate such a thing in wartime, and it was years before the secret was out.

The article above tells of strange happenings near an airfield during Word War Two.

21 What do you think was being developed?

22 How could the 'rays' detect aircraft?

23 What else are these waves used for?

Microwave oven

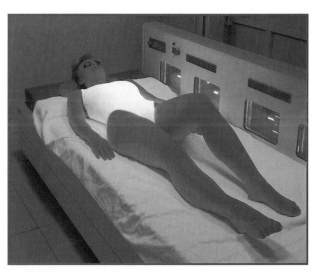
Ultraviolet lamps are used in this sunbed

P *1.12 Waves home and away*

In the Albert Hall, before recent improvements were made, there were areas where some sections of the orchestra could hardly be heard at all and others where the same note could be heard twice!

1 Write a letter to a newspaper criticizing the situation as it was. Suggest an explanation of what might have been happening. Include ideas on how the problems might be overcome.

Hint: the following words may help you:
reflection   echoes   diffraction   destructive interference

Medical waves

The article on the right gives information about some of the different uses of waves in a local hospital.

2 Which treatments use longitudinal waves?

3 Which treatments use transverse waves?

4 Which treatments use very short wavelength electromagnetic waves?

5 Where is there an example of the use of visible electromagnetic waves?

6 Of the electromagnetic waves used, which have the longest wavelengths?

7 Which treatments need very careful safety precautions because of radiation hazards?

8 Which ultrasound treatment do you think would use the highest power?

9 Why do you think cancer patients are turned to different angles when being treated with gamma radiation?

10 Design a chart which shows some of the medical uses of waves.

Waves for health

Prospective patients have every reason to be pleased with the range of wave equipment now available at Yeldwell General Hospital.

In addition to the usual X-ray facilities, the radiography department provides gamma ray treatment for cancer: the rays are used to kill cells in malignant tumours. Ultraviolet lamps are also available for the treatment of certain skin conditions.

The physiotherapy department offers a wide range of wave treatments. Infrared lamps help with a range of muscular disorders from stiff necks to sports-induced strains. Vibrations from ultrasound are used for the treatment of some muscular injuries. The latest wave treatment is in the hydrotherapy swimming pool, where waves provide variable resistance to movement as patients do exercises in the water. This allows weakened muscles to be built up gradually.

In the operating theatre, surgeons can now perform microsurgery using fine laser beams instead of scalpels.

Finally, many mothers are grateful for the ultrasound scan clinic which allows doctors to see images inside the womb without any risk to mother or baby.

Waves at home

The following devices can all be used in the home, but only with care: microwave oven, infrared lamp, ultraviolet lamp.

11 Find out what precautions have to be observed when using a microwave oven.

12 Why is it important to limit exposure to an ultraviolet lamp? Why must goggles be worn?

13 What precautions do you need to observe when using an infrared lamp?

Signals by 'phone

Telephone systems can use electrical signals travelling along cables, and light waves travelling along optical fibre cables. They can use microwaves and radio waves sent directly from transmitter to receiver or via satellites. The diagram below shows the different systems interconnecting.

14 If you were making a local telephone call what links might there be between you and the person you rang?

15 Suppose you wanted to ring an offshore island. What system might be used?

16 What links might be used if you were ringing another country?

17 Why can you detect no time delay when you are making a local call?

18 Why is there a small time delay when you are speaking to countries on the other side of the world?

Early radio

Hertz's first experiment with radio waves

The transmission of radio waves was first demonstrated by Heinrich Hertz in 1888. He showed that invisible electromagnetic waves were produced when an electric spark jumped across an air gap. To detect the waves, he used a large loop of wire, also with a gap in it. When the radio waves reached the loop, they generated a voltage which made a spark jump across that gap.

19 Imagine that time travel is possible! Write a letter to Hertz explaining why his discovery was so useful.

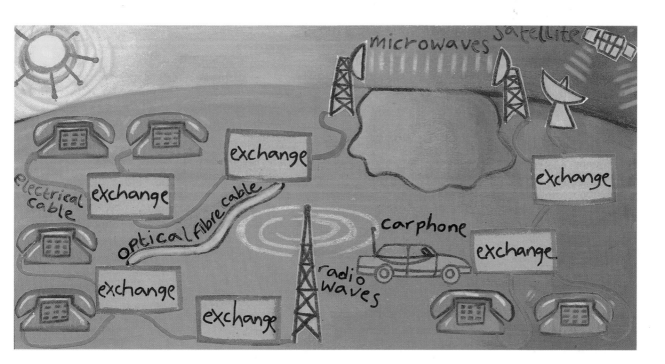

P 2.1 Looking into electricity

The electrical items shown in the picture change electrical energy into other forms.

1 List the different energy changes which are happening in the picture.

2 In the panels of data on the right below, what do 'V', 'W' and 'kW' stand for? What do they tell you about the item?

3 Decide which set of data matches each item in the picture.

4 Which items can be run on mains electricity? How can you tell from the data?

5 Which items might include logic circuits? Why?

6 How is the wire used in the elements of the electric fire different from the wire used in a power cable?

7 How does mains electricity reach your home?

8 What energy sources are used to generate electricity in power stations?

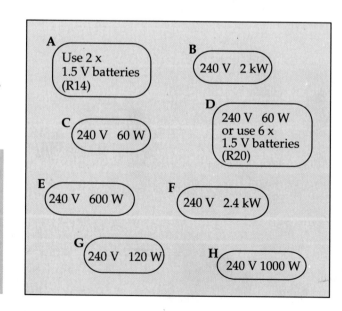

Connecting up

■ Connect up the following equipment so that the bulb can light:
  torch bulb   variable resistor
  2 batteries   connecting leads

■ What is the effect of the variable resistor?

■ Keep your circuit for the next investigation.

A
Use 2 x
1.5 V batteries
(R14)

B
240 V   2 kW

C
240 V   60 W

D
240 V   60 W
or use 6 x
1.5 V batteries
(R20)

E
240 V   600 W

F
240 V   2.4 kW

G
240 V   120 W

H
240 V 1000 W

Safety warning! Never attempt to investigate mains electricity, as it can kill.

Using an ammeter

The **current** (flow of electricity) in a circuit can be measured using an instrument called an **ammeter**.

9 What unit is current measured in?

10 What are the readings on the ammeters in the diagrams on the right?

■ Use an ammeter to measure the current in the last circuit you made. (If you are unsure about connecting the ammeter, read the end of the first page of spread P2.3).

■ What effect does the variable resistor have on the current?

■ What effect does the current have on the brightness of the bulb?

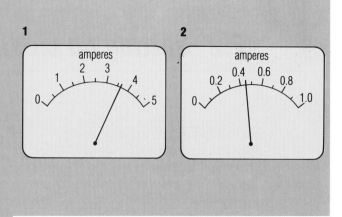

Making connections

The photograph on the right shows different types of cables, wires, plugs, connectors and switches.

11 Give an example of a circuit in which each of the items might be used?

12 Why do some cables contain more wires than others?

13 Why do some wires have a thicker covering than others?

14 What does the covering on the wires do?

15 Why are wires in cables often covered with materials of different colours?

16 Why do some plugs have three prongs and some only one prong?

17 See if you can classify the items in the picture by putting them into groups. You may be able to think of several ways of doing this.

18 Make a chart to show your ideas for classifying the items. Remember to name each group so it is clear why you have put those items together.

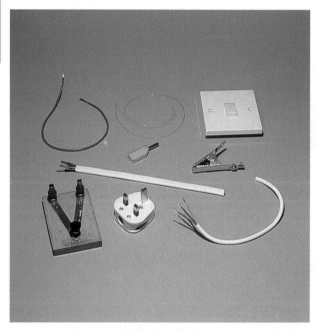

Just a few items from the huge range of cables, wires, plugs, connectors and switches available for electrical circuits. When selecting items like this, it is important to know which type of circuit each is suitable for.

Safety first

In the picture on the right, the kettle has an earth wire connected to its case, but the hair drier and the shaver do not. If you open the personal stereo, it is easy to touch the electrical contacts. And the model car has exposed conductors on its track! However, none of the items should give you a shock when being used.

19 Explain why each of the items should be safe to use.

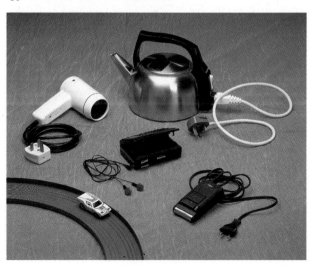

2.2 Setting up circuits

Model circuits

Anna works for a building company. She has been given the job of constructing a model house for a design exhibition. The house needs to be as realistic as possible, so Anna intends fitting lights, using small bulbs and switches. She wants a light in each room. She also wants a landing light which can be switched on and off from upstairs or downstairs. The whole system must work from a single set of batteries or from a low voltage power supply.

With your group, you have to plan the wiring system needed for the model house, then construct the circuits. The following questions may help you with your planning:

1 Can the lights in your home or school be switched on and off independently?

2 Look at the **series** and **parallel** circuits shown on the right. In which one can the lights be switched on and off independently? If you are not sure, set up the circuits and try them out.

3 Which of the two types of circuit would you use in the model house?

4 How do you think the problem of the landing light might be solved? You may have to search for more information to answer this.

Safety ! You must use a low voltage power supply such as a battery. The bulbs must be designed for the same low voltage.

What to do
- Plan your circuits on paper.
- Ask your teacher to check your plan.
- Make a list of the things you need.
- Set up your circuits. Test them to see if the lights work as you want them to.
- Make any changes that are needed.

Now you have to prepare some instructions which someone else could follow if they had to wire up the model house.

5 Draw a plan of your lighting circuits.

6 Prepare some written instructions to go with it. Remember to include any safety precautions which should be taken.

Bulbs (with switches) in series

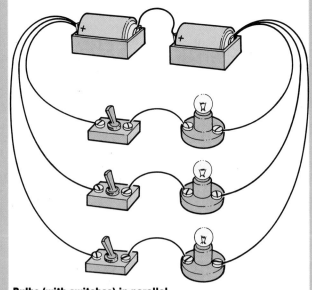

Bulbs (with switches) in parallel

Dimming the lights

When Anna constructed the model house, she found that the lights were very bright. She was worried that the heat from them might damage the model or start a fire. She decided that it would be useful if the lights could be dimmed when used for long periods.

With your group, plan different ways of dimming the lights. Try out some circuits to see how well they work.

Useful information
- Putting resistance wire in a circuit can reduce the current. Using a variable resistor is one way of changing the amount of resistance wire in the circuit.
- You can see one idea for a light-dimmer circuit on the right. When a variable resistor is connected in this way, it is called a **potentiometer**. Potentiometers are often used in electronic circuits for varying voltage. But you will need to investigate how suitable they are as light dimmers!

Things to think about
- Will you dim all the lights, or test out your ideas on one bulb?

Safety!
On certain settings, with powerful bulbs, parts of a variable resistor may become hot when a current passes through.

What to do
- ■ Draw up plans for different test circuits.
- ■ Get your plans checked and try them out.
- ■ Write a report on the different ways that the lights could be dimmed.

Dimmer switches in houses do not use variable resistors. Instead, they use an electronic device called a **triac**. This switches the bulb on and off very rapidly over and over again, but the change is so fast that the bulb glows without flickering. Turning the control knob changes the fraction of time the bulb is on or off. Short 'ons' and long 'offs' give a dim light. Longer 'ons' and shorter 'offs' give a brighter light.

7 Anna wanted the lights to be dimmed to prevent any risk of overheating. Does a variable resistor solve this problem?

8 Why do you think that variable resistors are not normally used in dimmer switches?

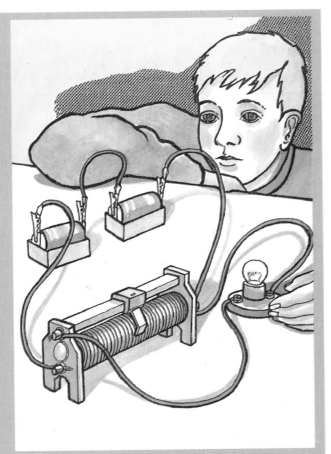

Connected like this, a variable resistor is called a potentiometer.

Spot the symbol

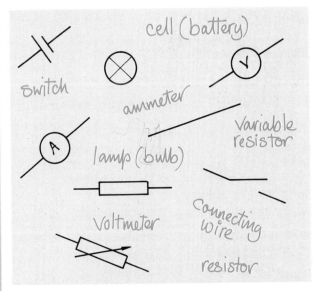

Above, you can see some electrical circuit symbols and names. However, these are all muddled up.

9 With your group, decide which label belongs with each symbol.

10 Make a chart to help you remember what the symbols mean.

Current ideas

In the diagram on the right, an ammeter is being used to measure the current in a part of the circuit near the batteries.

1 Draw the circuit using circuit symbols.
2 With your group, discuss what you think will happen to the size of the current as the electricity passes through each bulb. List your ideas.

Now carry out an investigation to test your ideas.

Useful information
• Before you set up the circuit, read the information at the bottom of the next column about connecting an ammeter.

What to do
■ Decide how you will test your ideas using only one ammeter.
■ Set up the circuit. Carry out your tests.
■ Write a report on what you found.

Changing the circuit

In the last investigation, two students wondered what would happen to the current if they changed the number of bulbs or batteries in the circuit. You can see their ideas on the right.

3 With your group, discuss whether you think each of the students' ideas is right or not.

Now test these ideas by experiment.

What to do
■ Draw the circuits which you will use.
■ Carry out your investigation.
■ Write a report on what you found.

Fading the lights

Some students want to build a puppet theatre.
■ Design and build circuits that could be used to make three bulbs fade like theatre lights.
■ Use an ammeter to measure the current from the battery.
■ What happens to the current as the lights fade?

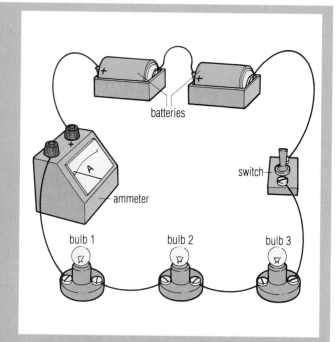

I think that the current will only get smaller if you use one battery instead of two

I think that the current will get smaller in a circuit with only two bulbs.

Connecting an ammeter

If you are using an ammeter with red and black terminals, you must make sure that it is connected into the circuit the right way round. The red (+) terminal of the ammeter should be on the same side of the circuit as the *positive* (+) end of the battery or the *red* (+) terminal of a low voltage power supply.

More currents

Three students have been having an argument about the currents in the circuit on the right. Below the diagram, you can see their ideas about the sizes of the currents in different parts of the circuit.

4 Do you agree with any of these ideas?

Test these ideas by setting up the circuit on the right and measuring the currents in the different parts.

Useful information
- When setting up a circuit, some people prefer to work from a **wiring diagram**, which looks like a picture. Others prefer a **circuit diagram** which uses symbols. There is an example of each type on the right at the bottom of the page. Choose whichever type suits you best.

Things to think about
- In what positions will you connect the ammeter? The wiring diagram and circuit diagram on this page show you one possibility.
- How will you check that the ammeter is connected the right way round each time?
- How will you record your readings?

What to do
- Draw a wiring diagram or circuit diagram for each position of the ammeter which you intend to use.
- Get your diagrams checked.
- Set up the circuit. Measure the current in different parts of the circuit and record your results.
- Which of the students' ideas do you agree with?
- Can you see any links between the current values you have measured?
- Make a report on what you have found out.

Particles on the move

A current of water consists of 'particles' of water moving along. Scientists think that an electric current also consists of a flow of tiny particles. The particles are electrically charged. They are so small that they flow through a wire by passing between its atoms.

5 See if you can find out the name of the tiny, charged particles that move along the wire in a circuit.

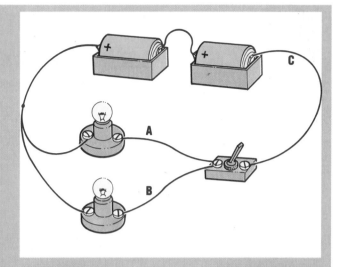

Wiring diagram

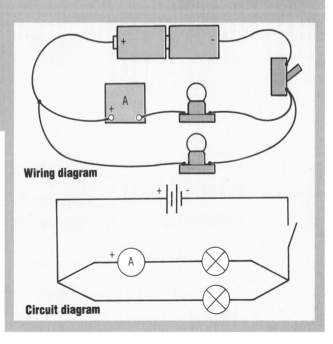

Circuit diagram

P 2.4 *Investigating voltage*

An electric current is made up of a flow of tiny, charged particles. Each particle carries energy with it. Look at the circuit on the right and discuss the following with your group:

1 What is giving the energy to the charged particles in the current?
2 Where will the charged particles have the most energy?
3 Where will they have the least energy?
4 What happens to the energy as the charged particles go through the bulb filament?
5 What difference would it make if the particles had less energy?
6 When choosing parts for a circuit like this, how can you make sure that the charged particles carry the right amount of energy to the bulb?
7 What will happen to the battery if the bulb is left connected for a long time?
8 How could you get the charged particles to have more energy?

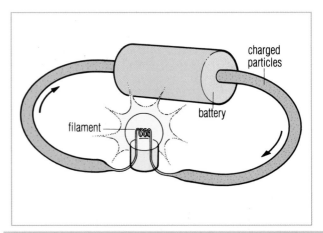

Checking the voltage

On the side of most batteries you will see a figure called the **voltage** printed. The higher the voltage, the more energy each charged particle is given by the battery. To measure the voltage, an instrument called a **voltmeter** is connected across the battery as in the photograph. The voltage is measured in **volts (V)**. Scientists sometimes say that there is a **voltage drop** across the battery.

9 One battery is marked '1.5 V', another is marked '9 V'. What does this tell you about the batteries? How do they compare?
10 If the voltage drop across a battery is lower than it should be, what does this tell you about the energy of its charged particles?

Find out if different batteries and low voltage power supplies give the voltages marked on them.

Useful information
• A voltmeter must be connected with its *red* (+) terminal towards the *positive* (+) of the battery or *red* terminal of the low voltage power supply.

Measuring the voltage of a battery

Safety!
check that the voltmeter is suitable for the battery or power supply you wish to connect it to. Never connect a voltmeter across the mains.

What to do
■ List the voltages marked on a variety of batteries and low voltage power supplies. (Each supply may have several settings.)
■ Measure the voltage drops across each battery or power supply.
■ Make a table to show how the measured voltages compare with the ones marked on the batteries and power supplies.

11 Can you think of any reasons why the measured voltages should be different from the marked ones? Discuss your ideas with your group.

Voltage drops round a circuit

Try measuring the voltage drops across different parts of the lighting circuit shown on the right. (Note that the circuit has been drawn in two different ways.)

Useful information
- A voltmeter must always be connected *across* the part where the voltage drop is to be measured.

What to do
- Draw your own diagram of the circuit. Make it larger than either of those on the right.
- Measure the voltage drop across any piece of connecting wire in the circuit. What result did you get?
- Measure the voltage drops across each of the bulbs and the battery. Mark these measurements on your diagram.
- Can you see any link between the voltage drops across the battery and the bulbs? Write a report on what you discovered.

Brighter lights

One student noticed that, with the circuit in the last investigation, the bulbs were not very bright. Her teacher challenged her to design a circuit to get the bulbs shining brightly. But she was only allowed to use the same bulbs and the same battery or power supply settings as before.

What to do
- Design the new circuit. Draw a diagram of it.
- Measure the voltage drops across the battery and each of the bulbs in your new circuit. Mark these measurements on your diagram.
- Can you see any links this time? Write a report on what you discovered.

True or false?

Paul wrote to a battery manufacturer complaining that one of their brand new batteries was giving a voltage which was less than the value marked on it. He had noticed this when using the battery to power a bulb. You can see the reply Paul received on the right. When he read it, wasn't sure that he believed it!
- Plan and carry out an investigation to check the battery manufacturer's claim.
- What did you discover?

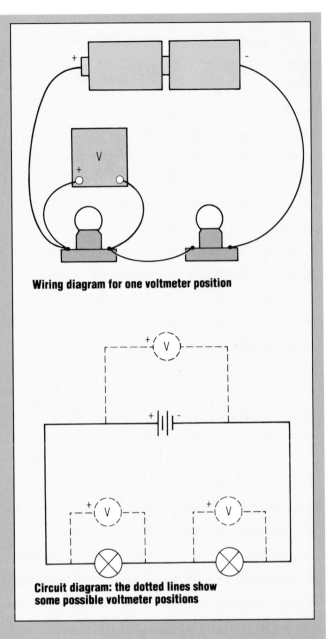

Wiring diagram for one voltmeter position

Circuit diagram: the dotted lines show some possible voltmeter positions

Dear Paul,

There is nothing wrong with your battery. We only print a voltage on the battery as a rough guide. The voltage can vary depending on how much current the battery is having to supply. Check this for yourself as follows. Measure the voltage across a battery. Now use two wires to connect a bulb to the battery. Measure the voltage again while the battery is making the bulb glow. You should notice a difference.

P 2.5 Switch on

Christmas trees often have their bulbs connected up like those in the circuit diagram beneath the photograph on the right. Discuss and answer the following with your group:

1 What type of circuit is shown, *series* or *parallel*?

2 What will happen if one of the bulbs in the circuit fails?

3 The bulbs are connected to a 240 V mains supply. What is the voltage drop across each bulb?

4 If 24 light bulbs were used in the circuit instead, what would be the voltage drop across each one?

5 If the bulbs were the same type as before, how would using 24 bulbs affect the brightness?

6 How could you get round this problem?

Car circuits

The circuit diagrams in the column on the right show two circuits used in a car.

7 In the circuit with the tail light bulbs, are the bulbs in *series* or in *parallel*?

8 What is the voltage drop across the demister when the switch is closed?

9 What is the voltage drop across each tail light bulb when the switch is closed?

10 If the tail light bulbs are switched on, how much current does the battery have to supply?

11 Redraw the circuits to show how the tail lights and the demister can both be supplied with power from the same battery.

The right voltage

On the right, you can see some information about three electrical items. One is designed to be used in the United States, where the mains voltage is just under a half that in the UK.

12 Which item is designed for the US mains supply?

13 Which item is designed for a car battery?

14 Which item do you think would use small batteries? How many 1.5 V batteries would be required for this item?

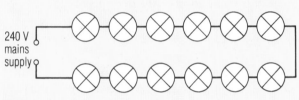

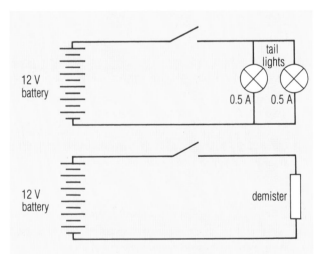

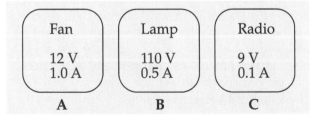

Modelling a circuit

Scientists often use **models** to help them describe and understand what is going on. On the right, you can see how one group of students thought it might be possible to model a series circuit. It is based on the idea of people going shopping. People collect money from the bank and then spend it at the shops.

With your group, discuss and answer the following questions:

15 In the model on the right, what do you think the people represent?

16 What does the bank represent?

17 What does the money handed out at the bank represent?

18 What do the shops represent?

19 What does the handing over of the money in the shops represent?

20 Do you think it is a good model?

Another group reckoned that they could adapt the model to show a parallel circuit. They would use the idea of a supermarket with lots of checkouts.

21 With your group, see if you can adapt the model for parallel circuits. Draw a large, labelled diagram to show your ideas.

22 See if you can use your model to explain some of the features of a parallel circuit.

Looking at switches

Switches in electrical circuits come in many shapes and sizes.

23 If possible, take a close look at some different types of switches.

24 Find out how they each work.

25 Describe how each switch works to another member of your group.

The diagram on the right shows part of the lighting circuit in a house. With your group, discuss and answer the following:

26 Are the bulbs in *series* or in *parallel*?

27 Are any of the bulbs in the diagram switched on? If so, which?

28 Can all the bulbs be operated independently? If not, which bulbs are controlled by the same switch?

29 What are the two-way switches used for?

30 How do the two-way switches work?

31 What is the voltage across each bulb when it is working?

32 Why is there a fuse in the circuit?

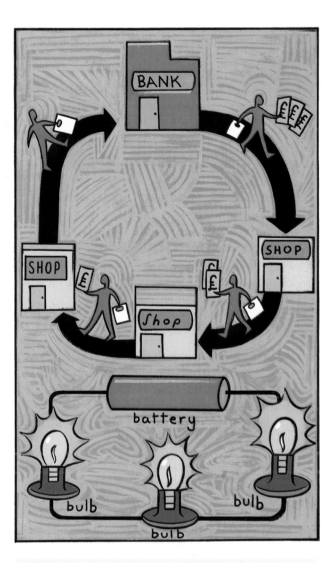

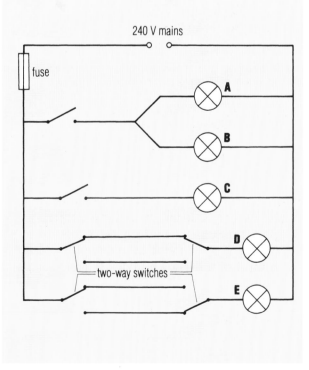

P 2.6 *Switches and gates*

A switch is a way of controlling a circuit. It is a simple form of **control unit**. In a house, most switches are turned on and off by hand. But some switches turn power on and off automatically.

1   Make a list of items in the house in which power may be switched on and off automatically.
2   For each item on your list, decide what change must occur to make the power switch on or off.

This iron is controlled by a bimetal thermostat similar to the one below

Automatic control

Electric irons are fitted with **thermostats**. A thermostat is a switch which is sensitive to heat. It switches ON when the temperature is too low and OFF when the temperature is too high.

3   Explain how a thermostat can keep an iron at a nearly steady temperature.
4   Why is it unable to keep the iron at an *exactly* steady temperature?
5   What other items of household equipment contain a thermostat?

The thermostat on the right contains a tiny **bimetal strip**, made of two different metals bonded together. When heated, one metal expands more than the other and the strip bends.

6   Which part of the thermostat detects the heat? What effect does the heat have?
7   Which part of the thermostat controls the power? How does it do this?

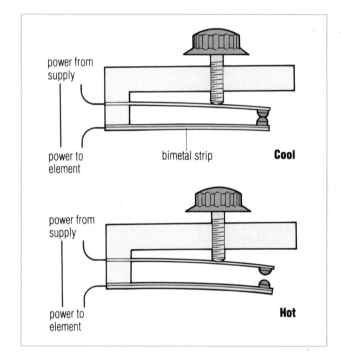

power from supply

power to element

bimetal strip   **Cool**

power from supply

power to element

Hot

Control systems

A bimetal thermostat is an example of a **control system**. The main parts of a control system are shown on the right.

Look again at the diagram of the bimetal thermostat connected to the heating element.

8   See if you can match the parts of this arrangement with the different parts of the control system shown in the diagram on the right.
9   Why do you think that part of the system is called 'feedback'?
10 What do you think would happen if a bimetal thermostat had no feedback?

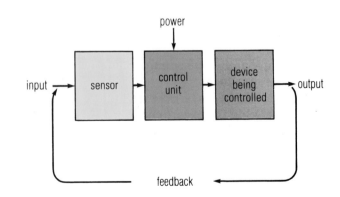

power

input → sensor → control unit → device being controlled → output

feedback

More automatic switching

The light in the photograph above contains an infrared sensor. At night, the light comes on if anyone approaches it.

11 How does the light detect that someone is near?

12 If a car drives up close, this may also make the light come on. Why?

The light in the photograph only works at night. It contains *two* automatic switches, one of which is controlled by the infrared sensor.

13 What type of sensor do you think controls the other switch?

Logic gates

Logic gates are electronic switches on microchips. Unlike ordinary switches, they need a power supply. Many gates have one or two inputs and one output. An input which is OFF becomes ON if connected to a small positive (+) voltage. Depending on the type of gate and the state of inputs, the output can also be OFF or ON. If ON, the voltage from the output can make other parts of a circuit work. Sometimes, scientists talk about inputs and outputs being LOW or HIGH rather than OFF or ON.

Microchip containing logic gates

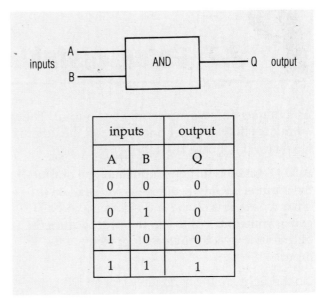

inputs		output
A	B	Q
0	0	0
0	1	0
1	0	0
1	1	1

The gate shown as a symbol above is called an **AND gate**. The **truth table** beneath it gives the output for every possible combination of inputs. **Logical 0** stands for OFF or LOW. **Logical 1** stands for ON or HIGH.

14 What input settings make the output HIGH?

15 Why do you think it is called an AND gate?

Investigating gates

There are specially designed plug-in modules for investigating logic gates. With modules like this, you know when an output is HIGH because an indicator light comes ON.

■ Use logic gate modules to investigate the properties of **OR** and **NOT** gates. Work out the truth tables for these gates.

The bulb in the circuit below is controlled by two ordinary switches in a box.

16 Work out a truth table for this circuit, using a 0 or a 1 to show whether each switch or the bulb is OFF or ON.

17 What type of gate are the switches in the box equivalent to?

18 What type of gate do you think the light in the photograph might contain? Why?

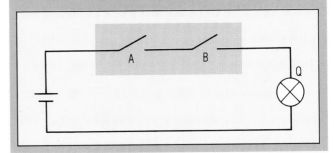

An **OR gate** has two inputs and one output. The output is HIGH if either one input *OR* the other is HIGH (or if both are HIGH).

A **NOT gate** has just one input and one output. If the input is HIGH the output is *NOT* HIGH (in other words, it is LOW) and vice versa. A NOT gate is sometimes called an **inverter** because the output is always the inverse (opposite) of the input.

On the right are the truth tables for an OR gate and a NOT gate.

1 Which table is for which type of gate?
2 If only one of the inputs of an OR gate is HIGH, what is the state of its output?

Table 1

inputs		output
A	B	Q
0	0	0
0	1	1
1	0	1
1	1	1

Table 2

inputs	output
A	Q
0	1
1	0

Investigating NAND and NOR gates

A **NAND gate** is equivalent to an AND gate followed by a NOT gate. A **NOR gate** is equivalent to an OR gate followed by a NOT gate. Both examples are shown on the right.

3 See if you can predict what the truth tables for a NAND gate and a NOR gate will be. Start by copying out the incomplete tables on the right (One line of one of the truth tables has been done for you).

■ Use logic gate modules to find the truth tables for NAND and NOR gates by experiment. Were your predictions correct?

By using NAND gates in different ways and combinations, it is possible to produce all the other types of gate. This idea is used in some electronic equipment to simplify the logic circuits. As an alternative, different gates can also be made using only NOR gates.

In the diagram on the right, the two inputs of a NAND gate have been connected together. This means that they are either both LOW or both HIGH.

4 Work out the truth table for the arrangement shown. Which type of gate do you think the arrangement is equivalent to?

■ Use logic gate modules to check your last prediction by experiment.

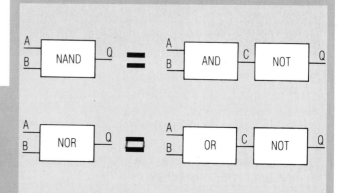

NAND gate

inputs			output
A	B	C	Q
0	0	0	1
0	1		
1	0		
1	1		

NOR gate

inputs			output
A	B	C	Q
0	0		
0	1		
1	0		
1	1		

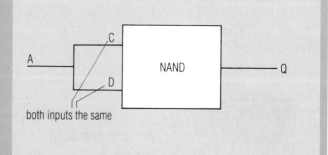

both inputs the same

Investigating a bistable

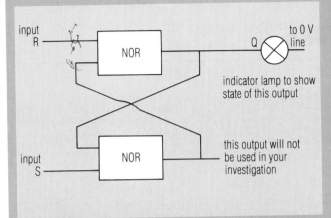

input R

NOR

to 0 V line

Q

indicator lamp to show state of this output

input S

NOR

this output will not be used in your investigation

The arrangement above is called a **bistable**. Two NOR gates have been interconnected so that there is feedback from the output of each to one input of the other. The bistable has special properties. You have to find out what they are! However, in this investigation, you will only be considering one of the outputs.

- Set up the bistable using logic gate modules.
- Make each input HIGH in turn. Do this several times. Work out a system for switching the output indicator light ON and OFF.
- Copy out the blank truth table below. Change the states of R and S in the order shown. Record the state of the output each time in your table. Remember: the output is HIGH if the output indicator light is ON.

inputs		output
R	S	Q
0	1	
0	0	
1	0	
0	0	
0	1	
0	0	

Look at your results and answer the following:

5 Does a bistable always give the same output if both inputs are LOW?
6 Imagine that you have just made one input HIGH, and the output indicator light has come ON. What will happen if that input then goes LOW again?
7 The inputs S and R are sometimes called the **set** and **reset** inputs. Why do you think they have been given these names?

An ordinary light switch can be in *either* of *two* stable positions, depending on how it was set when last pressed. The bistable you investigated also has two stable states. With both inputs 0, its output can be *either* 0 or 1, depending on the previous states of its inputs.

Bistables are a form of memory: they 'remember' their last output state. They are important in computers, where data is stored in memory as a series of binary numbers.

8 Why do you think that the circuit you have investigated is called a 'bistable'?
9 What are binary numbers?
10 Why are bistables important in computers?

Adding a relay

The output from a logic gate is too small to power equipment such as an electric motor. One way round the problem is to use an electrically operated switch called a **relay**:

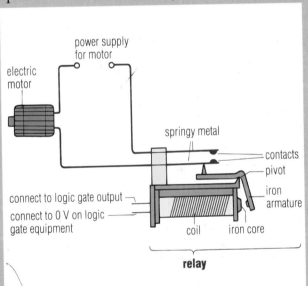

power supply for motor

electric motor

springy metal

contacts

pivot

connect to logic gate output

connect to 0 V on logic gate equipment

iron armature

coil

iron core

relay

Look at the diagram above.

11 If the logic gate output is HIGH, what effect does this have on the relay coil?
12 What effect does the relay coil then have on the armature?
13 How does this affect the motor circuit?

- Using a relay, and a bistable made from logic gate modules, build a circuit in which one input is used to switch an electric motor ON and the other to switch it OFF.

14 Can you think of any household electrical items which might use logic gates to control an electric motor in this way?

P 2.8 Resisting the flow

Wires are not perfect conductors of electricity. They resist the flow of current. Scientists say that they have **resistance**. And some wires have more resistance than others. In most circuits, the connecting wires need to have as low a resistance as possible. However, some appliances need wire which is specially designed to *provide* resistance. The resistance makes the charged particles lose energy when they flow through, and this energy is changed into another form. Wire which is specially designed to provide resistance is called **resistance wire**. The appliances in the pictures on the right contain coils of resistance wire.

1 What effect does the current have when it passes through each appliance?
2 What energy changes happen in each appliance when it is working?
3 Which part of each appliance contains the resistance wire?
4 What do you think happens to resistance wire when a current flows through it?
5 What other electrical items do you think might contain resistance wire?
6 When is light produced from electricity in a thunderstorm? What is resisting the flow of electricity then?

Resistors

You can see some **resistors** in the photograph on the right. Some of these are mounted, with other components, on a **circuit board**. There are some individual resistors laid out next to the circuit board.

Like resistance wire, resistors are specially designed to *provide* resistance. Many of them contain resistance wire. However, resistors do a different job from the resistance wire in hairdriers, electric fires and kettles. Resistors are used in electronic circuits to control the currents to different parts so that other components get the right amount of current to work properly.

7 What items at home or at school would you expect to contain circuit boards?
8 Why do designers of circuit boards have to think carefully about how their circuits can be kept cool?

These appliances all contain coils of resistance wire. Do you know where the resistance wire is and why it is used?

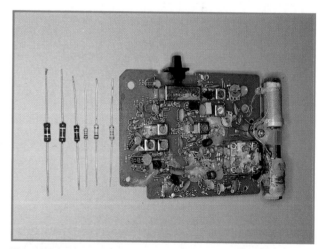

The components laid out next to the circuit board are resistors

Underwater coil

In the circuit on the right, the immersion heater contains a coil of resistance wire. Use the equipment shown to investigate the effect of passing a current through the coil.

What to do
- Read through the next two steps. Prepare a table for any readings you will take.
- Take the temperature of the cold water.
- Switch on the current. Take the temperature of the water every minute for ten minutes. Stir the water before you take each reading.
- Use your readings to plot a graph.
- Prepare a report on what you found.

More things to do
Here, you will need a meter to measure the current, and a low voltage power supply with different voltage settings.
- Investigate the effects of passing different currents through the heater. Remember to:
  - draw a diagram of the circuit.
  - make sure that your tests are fair.
  - check that the voltage of the power supply is suitable for the heater.

9 What difference does it make if you pass less current through the heater coil?

Resistors and current

Put different resistors in a circuit. Find out what happens to the current in the circuit if the resistance is increased.

Useful information
- Resistance is measured in ohms (Symbol Ω).
- You will need a circuit that contains a power supply, a resistor, and a meter for measuring the current through the resistor.
- Your teacher can supply you with a range of resistors of different resistances.

What to do
- Plan and draw your test circuit.
- Decide what measurements you need to make, and prepare a table for your readings.
- Decide what should be kept the same in each test so that your tests are fair.
- Carry out your investigation.

10 If the resistance in a circuit is increased, what effect does this have on the current?

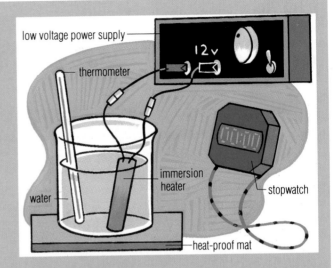

Rolling a resistor

Resistance putty contains particles of carbon. It can be rolled or moulded into different shapes.

11 What shapes do you think will give the most resistance? Long cylinders or short ones? Thick cylinders or thin ones?

- Test you ideas. Find out what factors affect the resistance.

Useful information
- Resistance putty can be connected into a circuit as shown in the diagram below.
- When shaping the putty, put it in a plastic bag, or wear rubber gloves, so that the carbon particles do not stain your hands.

Things to think about
- How can you tell from meter readings which shape has the most resistance? —

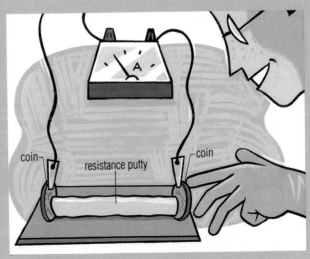

You should include a resistor (about 15 Ω) in this circuit

P 2.9 Voltage, current and resistance

Investigating a resistor

An electrical manufacturer wants to know what current will flow through a particular resistor when different voltages are put across it. The voltages will be from 0 to 6 V. The manufacturer does not want the resistor to heat up while being tested.

Find out how the current through a resistor depends on the voltage drop across it, making sure that the resistor does not heat up. Here is some possible equipment:

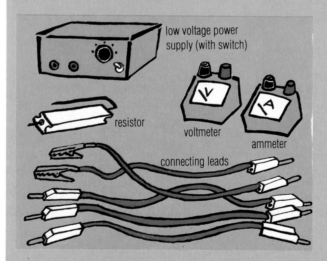

low voltage power supply (with switch)

resistor

voltmeter

ammeter

connecting leads

Useful information
- When planning a circuit, start by drawing a simple circuit with no meters in it. Then add the meters. Remember: voltmeters go *across* components; ammeters fit in the circuit so that all the current goes through them.
- To avoid temperature changes, switch your circuit on briefly to take each set of readings. Then switch it off again as soon as possible.

Things to think about
- How will you vary the voltage drop across your resistor? (Some low voltage power supplies have different settings so that you can vary the voltage.)
- How will you measure the voltage drop across the resistor?
- How will you measure the current through the resistor?

What to do
- Plan your circuit and get it checked.
- Prepare a table for your readings.
- Carry out the investigation and record your readings.
- Use your readings to plot a graph. Use the axes shown below, but choose numbers for the 'current' scale which will suit your own current readings.

You have now drawn a **current/voltage graph** for the resistor.
1 From your graph, describe how the current through the resistor changed as the voltage drop across it changed.
Keep your graph for later.

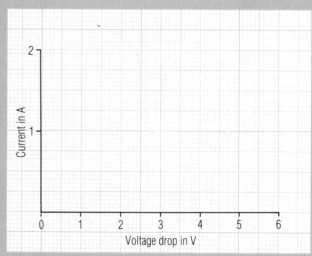

Investigating a bulb filament

The filament in a light bulb is a tiny coil of resistance wire, made of tungsten metal. Unlike the resistor you used before, the filament does *not* keep a steady temperature. It heats up - to more than 2500 °C!

Take readings so that you can plot a current/voltage graph for the filament of a light bulb (for example, a 12 V bulb).

Useful information
- If a bulb is marked '12 V', this tells you the *maximum* voltage which should be put across the bulb.

- Plan and draw your circuit. Decide how you will increase the voltage across the bulb in stages.
- Carry out your investigation and record your readings.
- Plot a current/voltage graph for the bulb.

From your graph:

2 Describe how the current through the filament changed as the voltage drop across it changed. *Keep your graph for later.*

Ohm's law

In 1826, George Ohm carried out some experiments with metal wires. He found that, provided the temperature does not change, the current through a metal wire is proportional to the voltage drop across it.
In other words....
if the voltage drop across a wire is doubled, the current doubles... and so on.

This is sometimes called **Ohm's law**. Resistors that behave like this are known as **ohmic resistors**.

3 Was the resistor in your first investigation an ohmic resistor?

4 What is special about the current/voltage graph of an ohmic resistor?

Calculating resistance

Scientists use an equation for calculating the resistance of a resistor:

$$\text{resistance} = \frac{\text{voltage drop across resistor}}{\text{current through resistor}}$$

In this equation, voltage is measured in volts (V), current in amperes (A) and resistance in ohms (Ω).

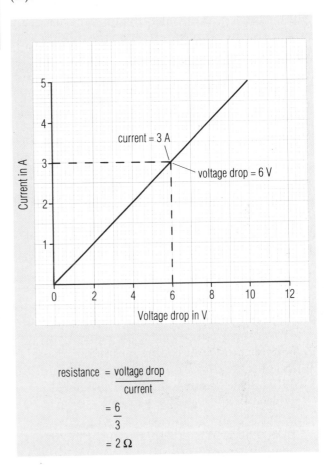

$$\text{resistance} = \frac{\text{voltage drop}}{\text{current}}$$
$$= \frac{6}{3}$$
$$= 2\,\Omega$$

Above, you can see how to calculate a resistance using a set of voltage and current values taken from a graph.

Start with your resistor graph:

5 Choose a set of voltage and current values. Use these to calculate the resistance.

6 Take two more sets of values from the graph. Calculate the resistance in each case.

7 Did the resistance of the resistor change? If so, how?

Now look at your bulb filament graph:

8 Choose three sets of values from this graph. Calculate the resistance in each case.

9 Did the resistance change as the filament heated up? If so, how?

Wiring a three pin plug

Plugs are a simple and safe way of connecting appliances to the mains supply. In the UK, square pin plugs are normally used. Different manufacturers produce slightly different designs, but the plug in the photograph on the right is typical:

The plug has connections for three wires, called **live**, **neutral** and **earth**. The live and the neutral form part of the circuit which carries power to the appliance. The earth is a safety wire.

The insulated coverings on the wires are colour coded so that you can tell which is which. The colours have been carefully chosen so that 'colour blind' people, who have problems telling some colours apart, can get the connections right. Wrong connections can be very dangerous.

1 What mistakes in the connections do you think could be dangerous?
2 When you look at a plug with no wires, how can you tell which is the earth pin?
3 How can you tell which is the live pin?
4 How can you tell which is the neutral pin?
5 What is the colour coding for the earth wire?
6 What is the colour coding for the live wire?
7 What is the colour coding for the neutral wire?
8 Why do some appliances need thicker cables than others? What might happen if too thin a cable was used?

Now wire a three pin plug to a short length of cable.

You need
Three pin plug, short length of cable, sharp knife, pliers or wire cutters, small screwdriver.

Safety warning!
You must not put your plug into a mains socket.
9 Why might this be dangerous?

Things to think about
• How much of the cable covering and the insulation round each wire will you remove?
• How will you make sure there are no loose strands of wire inside the plug?

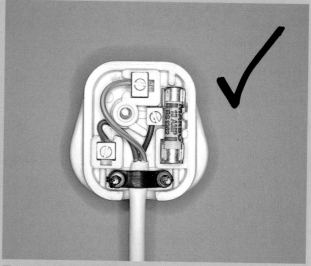

The right way to wire a plug

Useful information
• The cable grip stops the wires being pulled away from the pins if anyone tugs on the cable.

What to do
■ Wire your plug and get it checked.

The plug in the photograph below hasn't been wired properly.
10 What faults can you see? List the faults and say why each one is dangerous.

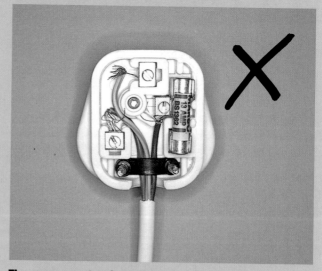

The wrong way to wire a plug

114

Choosing the right fuse

Three pin plugs sold in the UK are fitted with fuses.

11 Why are fuses needed?

12 How does a fuse work?

13 If a fuse is marked '13 A', what does this tell you about the fuse?

14 Why do different appliances need fuses of different values, like '3 A' and '13 A'?

On the right, you can see the circuit diagram for a floodlamp. The circuit is protected by a fuse. The fuse value needs to be slightly bigger than the current through the hot bulb. This is because a higher current passes through the bulb when it is first switched on.

15 Why is there a higher current through a bulb when it is first switched on?

16 Why might it be dangerous to fit a fuse whose value was a lot bigger than the current through the bulb?

17 What current is flowing through the bulb? (Hint: to calculate this, you can use the equation linking voltage, current and resistance in spread P2.9).

18 Which of these fuse values would you choose: 1 A, 3 A, 5 A or 13 A?

In some circuits, circuit breakers are used instead of fuses.

19 See if you can find out what the difference is between a circuit breaker and a fuse.

Earthing for safety

Our bodies are resistors! If we touch something at high voltage, the current through us may be enough to kill. An earth wire is a safety wire which allows current to flow harmlessly into the ground. Mains appliances with metal cases should always have an earth wire attached to the case.

The kettles on the right have each developed a fault so that the live wire is touching the case.

Look at the kettle *without* an earth wire:

20 What happens when the fault first develops?

21 What happens when someone touches the kettle?

Look at the kettle *with* an earth wire:

22 What happens when the fault first develops?

23 What happens when someone touches the kettle?

24 What needs to be done next?

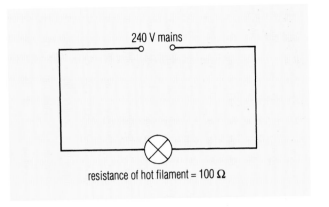

240 V mains

resistance of hot filament = 100 Ω

Kettle without earth wire

fault develops: live wire touches case

N
L

fuse

current flows through body

N
L

Kettle with earth wire

current flows to earth and blows fuse

case not live

circuit broken at fuse

P 3.1 Living with electricity

Safety warning! Never attempt to investigate mains electricity. Mains electricity can kill.

In the picture on the right, Jon is about to replace a light bulb.

1 With your group, list the things which Jon is doing wrong.
2 Prepare some instructions so that the bulb can be replaced without any sort of accident.

Jon has found two new bulbs in the cupboard. One is marked '240 V 60 W', the other is marked '240 V 100 W'.

3 What does the information tell you about the bulbs?
4 How would you decide which of the bulbs to use in place of the broken one?

A question of cost

Jon's family are worried by high electricity bills. They think that they are 'using too much electricity'. Jon's father reckons that some equipment uses more electricity than others, but he isn't sure how he can check on this. He wonders if the information printed on the different items might help. You can see some examples on the right.

5 Which numbers might help when deciding which items use most electricity?
6 What does the 'power' of an item tell you about it?
7 List the items on the right in order of power. Put the item that uses most power first. Leave a space alongside your list.

Jon's mother says that the amount of electricity each item uses also depends on how long it is switched on for.

8 With your group, estimate how long you think each item on the right will be used in a typical day. Put this information alongside the list you made in question **7** above.
9 Which three items do you think will use the most electricity?
10 How could you check which items used most electricity?
11 Make a poster giving your group's ideas on how to reduce the electricity bill at home.

| Colour TV | Hairdrier |
| 240 V 120 W | 240 V 1 kW |

| Fan heater | Refrigerator |
| 240 V 2 kW | 240 V 150 W |

| Electric kettle | Electric cooker |
| 240 V 2.4 kW | 240 V 9 kW |

| Table lamp | Immersion heater |
| 240 V 60 W | 240 V 3 kW |

Jon says that electricity flows in circuits. This means that the Electricity Board gets it back again, so it ought to be free! Jon's teacher says that when people pay their electricity bill, they aren't really paying for the 'electricity used'.

12 What *are* people paying for?
13 What answer would you give Jon?

Energy and power

Energy is measured in **joules (J)**.

Power is measured in **watts (W)**. Power tells you how quickly energy is being delivered.

A power of 1 watt means that energy is being delivered at the rate of 1 joule every second.

A power of 1 **kilowatt (kW)** means that energy is being delivered at the rate of 1000 joules every second.

Look at the table of information on this page about three appliances:

14 What energy changes take place when each appliance is working?

15 Which appliance will deliver the most energy in one hour?

16 What is the power of the heater in kW?

17 How many joules of energy will the hairdrier deliver every second?

18 How many joules of energy will the lamp deliver in 30 seconds?

19 How many joules of energy will it take to dry your hair if this takes 5 minutes?

20 How many joules of energy are delivered if you leave three 100 W lights switched on all night (10 hours)?

Appliance	Power in W
lamp	100
electric heater	3000
hairdrier	1000

Home hazards

The picture below shows some hazardous electrical situations. With your group:

21 List all the electrical hazards you can see in the picture.

22 Discuss why you think each situation is dangerous.

23 List your ideas for the safe use of electricity in the home.

Did you know?

A shock from the mains is particularly dangerous if the current flows from one hand to the other across the chest. Electricians sometimes work with one hand in a pocket to reduce the chances of this happening. A shock across the chest can stop the heart beating.

3.2 Electrical energy and power

Energy check

When people use mains electricity, the bill they receive is for the amount of energy supplied.

The head at Jon's school is concerned about the high electricity bills. The head thinks that electrical experiments in the science laboratories are the main cause. The head of science doesn't agree. She thinks that the electric heaters in the classrooms are the problem.

Do some checks yourself. Measure the electrical energy supplied when a low voltage immersion heater is used to heat some water for 5 minutes. Then calculate the electrical energy supplied when a 5 kW room heater is switched on for 5 minutes.

Useful information
- The top diagram shows how to use a **joulemeter** to measure the energy supplied to a low voltage immersion heater. The energy measurement is in joules.
- The bottom diagram shows how to measure the energy supplied if a joulemeter is not available. You have to calculate the power from ammeter and voltmeter readings:

  power = **voltage drop** x **current**
  (in watts)   (in volts)   (in amperes)

  Then you can calculate the energy supplied:

  energy = **power** x **time**
  (in joules)   (in watts)   (in seconds)

- *Safety warning! Do not connect any meters to electric mains heaters.*

What to do
- Draw a circuit diagram and prepare a table for your readings.
- Measure the energy supplied to the immersion heater in 5 minutes.
- Calculate the energy supplied to a 5 kW room heater in 5 minutes. (First, you will have to decide how many joules of energy are supplied to the heater every second.)

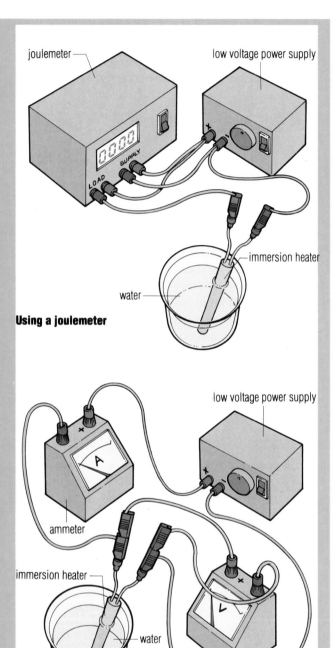

Using a joulemeter

Using a voltmeter and an ammeter

Now you can compare the two results:
1 Prepare a report explaining the conclusions you reached. (Remember that, in a school laboratory, there are usually many experiments going on at once).

Circuit calculations

Electrical energy is being supplied in each of the circuits on the right. Use the equations for power and energy to help you answer the following questions:

In *each* circuit:

2 What energy changes are happening?
3 How much power is being supplied?
4 How much electrical energy is supplied in 10 seconds?
5 How much electrical energy is supplied in 2 minutes?

Room heater

The sitting room at a day centre has an electric heater with two identical heating elements. Using switches, the elements can be connected to give different settings. In the column on the right, you can see diagrams showing the arrangements for the HIGH and MEDIUM settings.

6 The heater has a power of 4.8 kW when it is on the HIGH setting. What is this power in watts?
7 When the heater is on the HIGH setting, how are the elements arranged, in *series* or in *parallel*?
8 How many elements are being used when the heater is on the MEDIUM setting?
9 How should the switches be set for both elements to be OFF? Draw a diagram to show your answer?
10 How could the switches be set so that the elements are connected in *series*? Draw a diagram to show your answer. What name would you give to this setting?
11 What device could be fitted to the heater to help control the room temperature?

The following questions are about the heater when only *one* element is being used. The equations on the right at the bottom of the page will be helpful:

12 What is the power of the heater when only one element is being used?
13 If the mains voltage is 240 V, what is the current through the element? (Hint: what equation links power, voltage and current?)
14 How much energy is supplied in 1 hour? (Hint: what equation links energy, power and time?)
15 What is the resistance of the element? (Hint: what equation links voltage, current and resistance?)

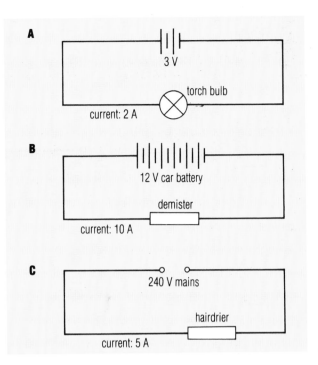

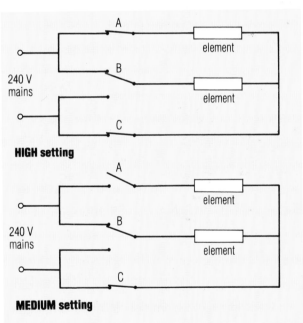

HIGH setting

MEDIUM setting

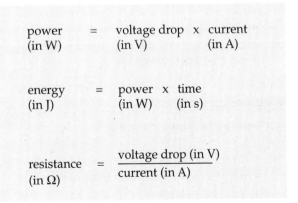

| power (in W) | = | voltage drop (in V) | x | current (in A) |

| energy (in J) | = | power (in W) | x | time (in s) |

$$\text{resistance (in } \Omega\text{)} = \frac{\text{voltage drop (in V)}}{\text{current (in A)}}$$

P 3.3 Counting the cost

One student said that electrical energy was measured in joules. Another said that this wasn't always the case. Her electricity meter at home measured energy, but it wasn't marked in joules.

1 What units would you find on the electricity meter at home?

Facing the bill

On the right, you can see the electricity bill which Ms Adams received. The amount of energy supplied is measured in **units**.

2 Why is it called a quarterly bill?
3 How many units were used in the quarter?
4 What is the charge per unit?
5 How did the Electricity Board calculate the cost of the energy supplied?

Counting the kWh

The unit of energy on an electricity bill has another name. It is called a **kilowatt hour.**
1 kilowatt hour (kWh) is the energy supplied if a 1 kilowatt (kW) appliance is used for one hour.

A student listed the powers of some electrical appliances in her home. She estimated how long each was switched on for during one week. Then she calculated the number of kWh used by each appliance and put the results in a table. You can see an incomplete version of this table on the right:

6 How did the student calculate the number of kWh supplied in each case?
7 Copy the table. Complete it by putting in the missing figures.
8 What was the *total* energy (in kWh) that was supplied to all the appliances during the week?
9 If the energy costs 8p per unit, what was the total cost for the week?

In the previous spread, you calculated energy in joules using this equation:

energy = power x time

10 Can this equation also be used for calculating energy in kWh? Explain your answer by giving an example.

CENTRAL ELECTRICITY BOARD
VAT REG NO 3387449 45

MS S ADAMS
3 WINDRIDGE AVE   REF
WITTON   3853 401
BS17 8TQ

METER READINGS		UNITS	COST (p)	
PRESENT	54120	USED	PER UNIT	£
PREVIOUS	52369	1751	8.00	140.08

QUARTERLY CHARGE   12.20
VAT   0.00

AMOUNT DUE   152.28

Appliance	Power	Hours used in one week	kWh
Fan heater	2 kW	10	20
Table lamp	100 W	15	1.5
Hairdrier	1 kW	1	
Iron	1 kW	2	
Kettle	2.4 kW	2	
Microwave oven	500 W	5	
Colour TV	120 W	10	
Stereo	50 W	12	

Comparing energy units

The joule and the kWh are both units of energy.
1 kWh is the same as 3 600 000 joules.

11 Why do you think that the Electricity Board measures energy in units (kWh) rather than in joules?

Phil's flat

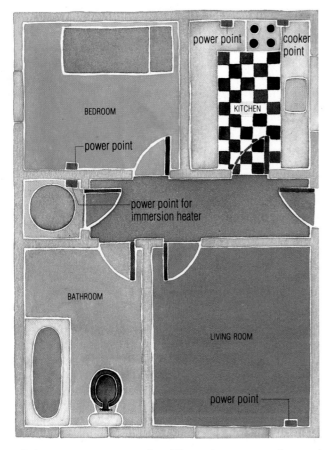

Phil is going to rent a flat. There is no central heating and no gas supply, so all the heating and cooking will be by electricity. The plan above shows you where all the power points are situated.

12 Why is there no power point in the bathroom?

13 How is a bathroom light switch different from other light switches? Why is it different?

14 Make a list of all the electrical equipment that you think Phil might want in his flat.

15 Which *two* items do you think would cost most to run?

16 Which *two* items do you think would cost least to run?

17 Are there enough sockets for all the items on your list? If not, how can the problem be solved without fitting extra sockets?

Phil is not happy with the way he is having to use adaptors and extension leads.

18 What are the dangers of using adaptors so that several plugs will fit in one socket?

19 Why can extension leads be dangerous?

20 If Phil could install two extra sockets, where do you think these should go?

Plugs on household appliances are normally fitted with either a 3 A or a 13 A fuse.

21 Go through the list of appliances in the table on the opposite page. Decide which fuse should be used for each of these items. How did you make your decision?

Phil's cooker

The photograph below shows you the powers of the different parts of Phil's cooker.

22 What is the power of each plate in kW?

23 Are the different parts connected in *series* or in *parallel*?

24 What is the total power of the cooker?

25 If the cooker is used with everything switched on for 2 hours, how much energy is supplied (in kWh)?

26 Estimate how much you think it will cost Phil to run his cooker for a week. (Assume that one unit costs 8p).

27 What is the current through each part of the cooker? (Mains voltage is 240 V.)

28 What is the total current when everything is switched on?

29 The cable to a cooker is permanently wired to the mains supply. Why do you think a cooker does not have a fused plug which can be pushed into a socket?

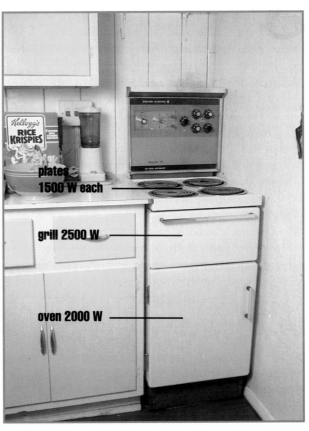

plates 1500 W each

grill 2500 W

oven 2000 W

P 4.1 A closer look

Scientists try to make sense of what they observe by thinking up **models** to describe what is happening. You may remember the particle model of matter. The ideas on the right should help to remind you.

1 With your group, discuss all the different things that the particle model helps to explain. Make a list of your ideas.

Looking at models

People sometimes ask: 'What is electricity?' The reports on the right are about models which have helped develop our understanding of electricity. Read them. Then discuss and answer the following with your group:

2 In Volta's model what does an electric current consist of?

3 In Volta's model, which way does the current flow? Draw a diagram of a circuit with a battery and a bulb. Mark on the positive and negative terminals of the battery. Show the direction of the current according to Volta's model.

4 What particle did Thomson discover?

5 Where does this particle come from and what type of electric charge does it carry?

6 According to Thomson's model, what does an electric current consist of?

7 What is Rutherford's model of the atom? Draw a diagram to show this model.

8 In Rutherford's model, which do you think might escape from an atom more easily, the *nucleus* or an *electron*? Do you think that this model supports Thomson's idea of what an electric current is?

9 Redraw your diagram of a circuit with a battery and a bulb. Mark on the positive and negative terminals of the battery. This time, show the direction of electron flow. Is this the same as the current direction in Volta's model?

Today, scientists still use a model of the atom which includes electrons and a nucleus. But it is a mathematical model based on the equations of **quantum mechanics**, and cannot really be described using pictures.

Everything is made of particles.

The particles are very small.

The particles are always in motion.

The particles do not change size.

1800

Alessandro Volta produces electricity using a battery made from silver, zinc and brine. The battery gives him a small shock when he links the terminals by touching them. Volta suggests that a current is flowing. According to his model, the current is an invisible fluid which flows from the **positive (+)** terminal round to the **negative (-)** terminal.

1897

J.J. Thomson discovers tiny particles with a negative (-) charge that are smaller than atoms. He calls these particles **electrons**. His experiments suggest that an electric current is a flow of electrons. Having a negative charge, electrons are repelled from the negative terminal of a battery and attracted round the circuit to the positive terminal.

1904

Thomson's work indicates that all atoms contain electrons. If there is a current, electrons are escaping from atoms and are on the move. Thomson proposes a 'pudding' model of the atom: each atom consists of a lump of positively charged material with negatively charged electrons dotted through it like raisins in a steamed pudding.

1911

Ernest Rutherford proposes a new model of the atom based on the results of his experiments. In this model each atom has a tiny, dense nucleus at its centre. The **nucleus** has a positive charge. Around the nucleus, electrons orbit rather like planets orbiting the Sun.

Looking at directions

When dealing with metal conductors, scientists now use the electron flow model of a circuit, first developed by Thomson. According to this model, the current is a flow of electrons moving from the negative terminal of a battery round to the positive terminal. This flow is shown in the diagram on the right.

The current direction in Volta's original model is now called the **conventional direction**. It is still used in circuit diagrams, where it is shown using arrowheads on the circuit itself. The arrowheads are helpful when following complicated circuit diagrams. They mark the path from the positive terminal of the power supply round to the negative.

10　Look at other textbooks which deal with electricity. Find out if they use the conventional direction or electron flow in their circuit diagrams.

Energy changes

Look at the circuit diagram above the photograph on the right:

11　What energy changes are taking place in the bulb?

12　What energy changes are happening in the battery?

13　What type of energy do the electrons in the wire have?

14　Describe what happens to an electron as it goes round the circuit.

Charge and current

Electrons each carry the same amount of electric charge. Scientists measure charge in **coulombs** (**C**). One coulomb is the charge carried by about six million million million electrons! However, there is a more accurate way of saying what a coulomb is:

One coulomb is the charge supplied if a current of 1 ampere (A) flows for 1 second.

15　How much charge (in coulombs) would a battery supply if it delivered a current of 2 A for 1 second?

16　How much charge (in coulombs) would a battery supply if it delivered a current of 2 A for 3 seconds?

17　How much charge (in coulombs) would a battery supply if it delivered a current of 4 A for 6 seconds?

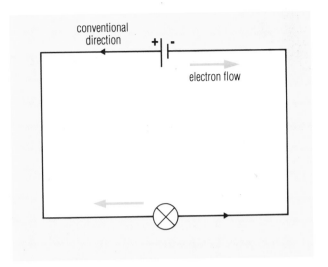

Over a million million million million million electrons in action

Scientists use an equation for calculating amounts of charge:

charge	=	current	x	time
(in coulombs)		(in amperes)		(in seconds)

18　Use this equation to work out the answers to questions **16** and **17** again. Are your new answers the same as the ones you had before?

19　If 3 coulombs leave a battery every second, what is the current in amperes?

20　If a battery supplies 12 coulombs in 3 seconds, what is the current in amperes?

P 4.2 Electrons on the move

In this spread, you are going to take a closer look at how scientists model the behaviour of an electric current in a circuit.

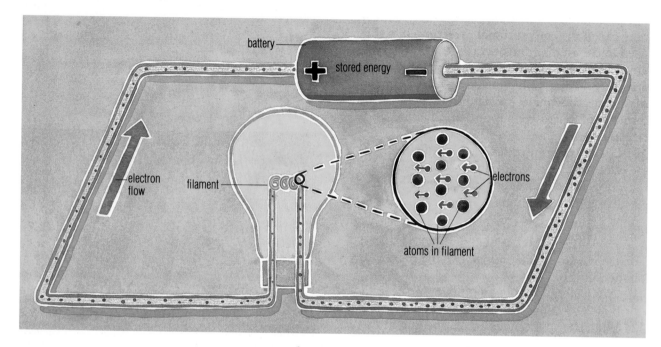

In the diagram above, a bulb is connected to a battery. The filament of the bulb is a coiled-up length of thin resistance wire made of tungsten metal. Like atoms in all solids, the tungsten atoms are vibrating. The higher the temperature, the faster they vibrate:

1 What is pushing the electrons through the filament?
2 What will happen to the tungsten atoms when the electrons bump into them?
3 What effect will this have on the temperature of the filament?
4 What is *gaining* energy in the filament?
5 What is *losing* energy in the filament?

The electrons are being pushed out of the battery into a wire. In this wire, they are squashed closer together, rather like the coils of a compressed spring. They pass through the filament and then return to the battery through another wire.

6 When do the electrons have most energy?
7 Where does this energy come from?
8 What type of energy do the electrons have when they leave the battery?
9 What happens to this energy?

Voltage, charge and energy

A battery gives electrons energy which they 'spend' in different parts of the circuit.

A 1 volt battery gives 1 joule of energy to each coulomb of charge it delivers.
A 2 volt battery gives 2 joules of energy to each coulomb of charge it delivers......

Scientists express this idea in the form of an equation:

energy supplied = charge delivered x voltage
(in joules)   (in coulombs)   (in volts)

Veena's car has a 12 V battery. When she starts the car up in the morning, the battery supplies energy to the starter motor.

10 How much energy does the battery give to each coulomb of charge it delivers?
11 Veena turns the ignition key to start up. When she does this, the battery delivers 100 coulombs of charge. How much energy is the battery supplying?
12 In the starter motor, what type of energy is this changed into?

Crossing the gap?

Parminder knew that, in a television set, the picture is made by a beam of electrons which moves quickly over the back of the screen and makes it glow. He also knew that there was a vacuum (no air) in a TV tube. He wondered if this meant that electrons could sometimes escape from wires and move across gaps.

13 The photographs **A** and **B** on the right show two other situations where a moving beam of electrons is being used to form an image on a screen. What equipment is each photograph showing?

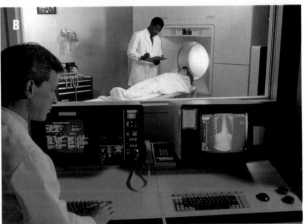

The diagram under the photograph shows the equipment which Parminder's teacher demonstrated at school. There is a glass bulb with no air in it. Inside, are two metal **electrodes**, called the **anode** and the **cathode**. The cathode is a filament, just like the one in a light bulb. It can be heated by switching on a 6 V supply. The high voltage power supply can be connected either way round, making the anode positive and the cathode negative, or vice versa. A sensitive meter shows if there is any current flowing in the circuit.

14 Why might you expect the meter in the diagram to be reading zero?

The table on the right at the bottom of the page shows what happened when Parminder's teacher used the equipment in an experiment.

15 For a current to flow, did the cathode have to be *hot* or *cold*?

16 For a current to flow, did the cathode have to be *negative* (-) or *positive* (+)?

17 Does the experiment show that electrons can move across a gap?

Scientists think that, when the cathode is hot, electrons in the metal have enough energy to escape. The effect is called **thermionic emission**. Once the electrons have left the cathode, they can be pulled across the empty space to the anode, provided the high voltage connections are the right way round.

18 To pull the electrons across, does the anode have to be *negative* or *positive*?

19 What does this tell you about the type of charge on an electron?

Thermionic emission is used in a TV tube. Electrons escaping from a cathode are focused into a fine beam which hits the screen and makes it glow. Colour TVs use three beams to produce the colours red, green and blue on the screen.

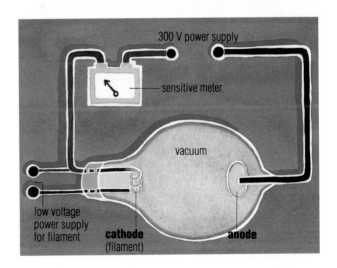

Cathode		Anode	Current in mA
cold	−	+	0
cold	+	−	0
hot	−	+	50
hot	+	−	0

125

In 1895, Wilhelm Roentgen was investigating how electricity passed through a gas. He was using a glass tube containing a gas at low pressure and two electrodes with a very high voltage across them. While using the equipment he made a surprise discovery.

First, he noticed a green glow in another part of his darkened laboratory. The glow was coming from a sheet of cardboard which had been coated with chemicals similar to those now used on a TV screen. When Roentgen put his hand in front of the cardboard, parts of the glow faded and he saw a shadow of his bones! Later, he discovered some 'fogged' photographic plates in a box near the tube. The plates had apparently been exposed, yet they were wrapped in black paper!

Roentgen realised that his tube was giving off an invisible, penetrating radiation. He called this radiation **X-rays**. Scientists now know that the X-rays were being produced when high-speed electrons hit the far end of the tube. The electrons were losing energy and some of this was being emitted as radiation.

When Roentgen first investigated X-rays, he was not aware of the dangers of being exposed to the radiation.

1 What made Roentgen think that the rays he had discovered were penetrating?
2 What material did the X-rays *not* pass through easily?
3 What effects did the X-rays have on the cardboard coating and on the photographic plates?
4 How could Roentgen be sure that these effects were not caused by light?
5 When Roentgen discovered X-rays, he immediately realised that they would have important medical uses. Why?

The report on the right describes some of the hazards faced by early experimenters with X-rays.
6 What did these early experimenters *not* know about X-rays which would have been important for their health?
7 Why do you think early experimenters often suffered medical problems with their fingers and hands?
8 Why is modern X-ray equipment much safer for researchers, medical staff and patients?

X-RAY DANGERS

Unknown hazards faced by early experimenters.

In the early days of X-ray research, experimenters were quite unaware of the dangers they faced from the radiation. In later years, many would die of cancer. Others would suffer from deformed fingers and growths on their hands.

When X-rays are absorbed they can cause cell damage inside the body. X-rays are an essential tool in medical work but, today, exposure to them is kept to the absolute minimum. Lead shielding is used to absorb stray radiation from the equipment, and X-ray photographs are taken using very short exposure times.

A modern X-ray tube

The diagram on the right shows one type of modern X-ray tube. Unlike early tubes, this one has a vacuum in it rather than a low pressure gas. The cathode contains a filament which is heated by a current. A very high voltage (at least 60 000 volts) is applied between the cathode and the anode. This pulls electrons away from the cathode and towards the anode. The electrons hit the anode (also called the **target**) at high speed. Most of their energy is converted into heat, so the target becomes extremely hot. A small amount of energy is emitted as X-rays.

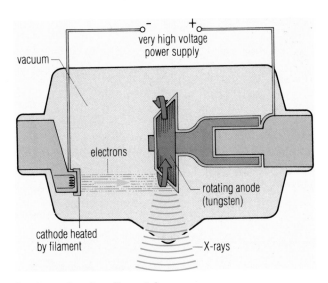

One type of modern X-ray tube

9 Why do you think there has to be a vacuum in the tube?
10 Why is the cathode heated?
11 Why must the cathode be negative (-) and the anode positive (+)?
12 What type of energy do the electrons have before they hit the target?
13 What happens to this energy when the electrons hit the target?
14 In the type of X-ray tube shown, the target is rotated when the tube is working. Why do you think it is rotated?

X-ray photographs

On the right, you can see an X-ray photograph of part of the body. Unlike an ordinary photograph, it is printed as a negative. The white areas in the picture are those which the radiation has *not* passed through.

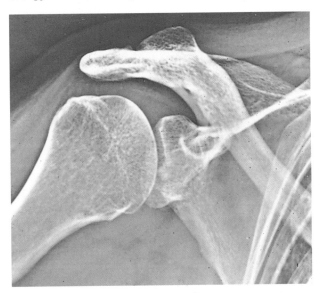

15 Which do you think X-rays penetrate most easily, bone or soft tissue?
16 Why, when an X-ray photograph is taken, are people only exposed to the radiation for a fraction of a second?
17 If the tube voltage is increased, the X-rays have shorter wavelengths and become more penetrating. Why would extremely high voltages not necessarily be useful for taking medical X-ray photographs?
18 What other methods do you know of for seeing images inside the body? Are these safer or more dangerous than X-rays?

Part of the family

X-rays are just one member of the electromagnetic family of waves.

19 What other types of electromagnetic radiation can you name? Are any of these as penetrating as X-rays?

Scientists think that electromagnetic waves are produced whenever charged particles (such as electrons) vibrate or lose energy.

20 See if you can decide which type of waves are being produced in each of the examples **A**, **B** and **C** below.

A	Electronic circuits make electrons vibrate in an aerial. This produces invisible waves which can be used for transmitting sounds and pictures over long distances.
B	Atoms in a very hot material vibrate, making the electrons change positions and lose energy. The radiation emitted can be detected by the eye.
C	Electrons vibrate in a cavity inside a device called a **magnetron**. The radiation emitted is absorbed by food which is heated up as a result.

Q Life and health

Q 1.1 Pass it on

People often look at babies and say 'Oh, she's got her father's nose,' or 'Hasn't he got his mother's eyes?'

1   What do you think they mean by this?

The photographs on this page show people with different physical characteristics.

2   Decide what are the main characteristics shown in each photograph and write them down.

Parents pass on some of their physical characteristics to their children.

3   From the characteristics shown in the photographs, discuss and write down your ideas about the following:
- Which characteristics would definitely be passed on to a child?
- Which characteristics would definitely not be passed on?
- Which ones are you not sure about?

4   Why do you think children sometimes have similar talents to their parents?

5   Why do you think brothers and sisters sometimes have similar talents?

6   Why do you think brothers and sisters may have different talents, and may be good at things their parents cannot do?

Seeing the difference

A gardener collected seeds from one plant and sowed them in different parts of his garden. He also gave some to his friends. When the seeds grew, he was surprised to find how different the plants looked.

7 Why do you think the plants were different? How many reasons can you think of?

8 What do you think would have happened if the gardener had sown the seeds in the same type of soil in the same part of the garden?

Twins

On the right, there is some information about **genes**. Below, there is a diagram which shows how characteristics are passed from parents to their children when these are twins.

9 Use this information to explain why some twins are identical and others are not. Try to use the word 'genes' in your explanation.

10 Why are ordinary brothers and sisters not identical, but often a little bit like each other and their parents?

11 In what ways are you similar to others in your family? As well as thinking about your appearance, think about things you like doing or are good at.

12 Which similarities do you think are due to the gene code and which are due to the environment in which you live?

Genes

Deep inside the cells of all living things are tiny chains of chemicals. These form a code which carries information about the living thing and many of its characteristics. The different parts of this coded information are called **genes**. Every cell carries many genes. They are not only a code for physical characteristics like hair colour. They are also a code for making all the vital substances which the body needs to live and grow.

You will find out more about genes later in the module.

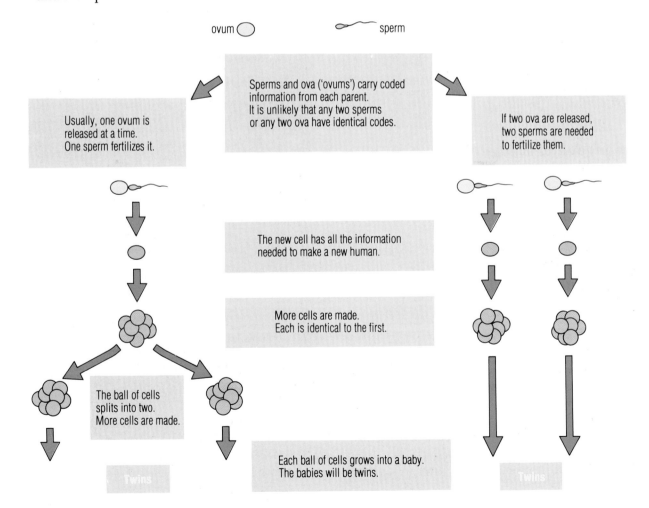

ovum ◯   ✐ sperm

Sperms and ova ('ovums') carry coded information from each parent. It is unlikely that any two sperms or any two ova have identical codes.

Usually, one ovum is released at a time. One sperm fertilizes it.

If two ova are released, two sperms are needed to fertilize them.

The new cell has all the information needed to make a new human.

More cells are made. Each is identical to the first.

The ball of cells splits into two. More cells are made.

Each ball of cells grows into a baby. The babies will be twins.

Twins   Twins

131

 **1.2 Mendel's experiments**

Gregor Mendel was an Austrian monk. In the 1860s, he made important discoveries about the way characteristics are inherited. He did so by carrying out pollination experiments on different varieties of pea plant.

Pollination

In the **ovary** of a flower, an **ovule** can develop into a seed, but only if a male **gamete** (sex cell) from a grain of **pollen** combines with a female gamete in the ovule. First, pollen must be transferred from an **anther**, where it was stored, to a **stigma**. This is called **pollination**. The pollen may come from the same plant or from a different plant.

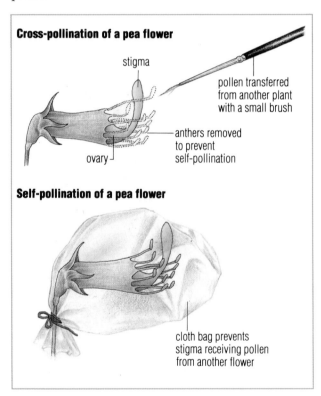

Cross-pollination of a pea flower

stigma

pollen transferred from another plant with a small brush

anthers removed to prevent self-pollination

ovary

Self-pollination of a pea flower

cloth bag prevents stigma receiving pollen from another flower

1 What is the difference between self-pollination and cross-pollination?
2 In experiments, how can scientists make sure that a plant is cross-pollinated?
3 In experiments, how can scientists make sure that a plant is self-pollinated?
4 What does a pollen grain do after it has stuck to a stigma?

Crossing experiments

Mendel tried **crossing** (cross-pollinating) pea plants to find out which characteristics were inherited by their offspring ('children'). In each experiment, he concentrated on a single characteristic: for example, whether the plants had round or wrinkled seeds. But he always started with **pure-breeding** varieties. These were plants which had been self-pollinated for many generations so that all the offspring had the same characteristic as the parent. This is how he might have described his results in English today:

❝ When I crossed two pure-breeding round-seed plants, all the offspring were the same as the parents. This happened with other characteristics as well. But when I crossed round-seed plants with wrinkled-seed plants, all the offspring were round-seed plants. This surprised me. I had expected them to be halfway between the two. When I crossed green-pod plants with yellow-pod plants, all the offspring were green-pod plants. ❞

Here is a way of showing some of these results:

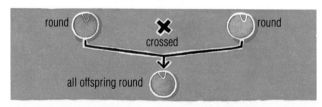

round ✖ round
crossed
all offspring round

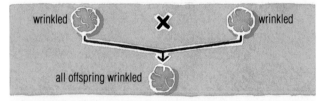

wrinkled ✖ wrinkled
all offspring wrinkled

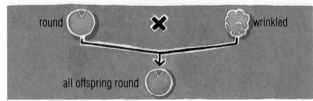

round ✖ wrinkled
all offspring round

5 Draw diagrams like those above to show the results of crossing the following pure-breeding plants: **a** a yellow-pod plant with another yellow-pod plant **b** a yellow-pod plant with a green-pod plant.

Testing a hypothesis

Mendel put forward a **hypothesis** (untested theory) to explain his results:

❝ I think that plants have tiny particles in them which carry coded information about their characteristics. For each characteristic, they inherit *two* particles, one from each parent. In pure-breeding plants, these particles are the same. But in other plants, they may be different. If they are different, one particle masks the other. For example, a round-seed particle masks a wrinkled-seed particle. Round is **dominant** over wrinkled. So the offspring becomes a round-seed plant:

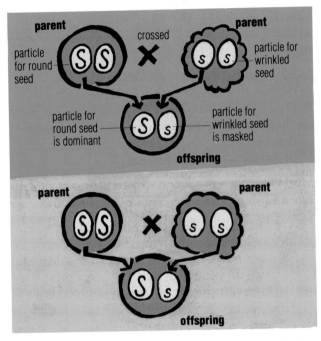

Pollen grains and ovules have only *one* particle for each characteristic. It could be either of the particles in the parent. It is all a matter of chance. On average, half the pollen grains have one of the particles and half have the other. The same is true with ovules. ❞

6   The diagram above shows two possible ways in which particles could be inherited. Are there any other combinations? If so, do they all produce round-seed plants?

The offspring from pure breeding plants which have been crossed are called the **first filial generation** (F_1 for short). To test his hypothesis, Mendel decided to **self** (self-pollinate) the offspring. The result was the **second filial generation** (F_2 for short). At the top of the next column, you can see one possible combination of particles in the offspring. But there are others!

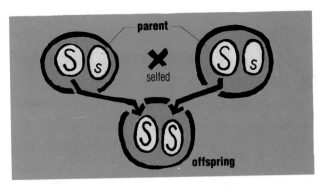

In this example, a single plant acts as both parents because it has been self-pollinated.

7   Draw your own version of the diagram above. Then draw all the other combinations (remember: there must be one particle from each 'parent'.) Make sure you show which characteristic each offspring has.

8   How many combinations are there altogether? How many produce round-seed plants? How many produce wrinkled-seed plants?

In his experiments, Mendel grew thousands of F_2 plants and counted the number with each characteristic. Here are some of his results:

Characteristic	Numbers of F_2 offspring	
Form of seed	round: 5474	wrinkled: 1850
Colour of pod (unripe)	green: 428	yellow: 152
Length of stem	long: 787	short: 277
Colour of seed coat	grey-brown: 705	white: 224
Position of flowers	side of stem: 651	end of stem: 207

9   Divide the number of F_2 round-seed plants by the number of F_2 wrinkled-seed ones. What number do you get?

10 Does this result support Mendel's hypothesis? Explain your answer.

11 Do the other results support Mendel's hypothesis?

12 How would you explain any difference between Mendel's results and what his hypothesis seems to predict?

Q 1.3 Explaining Mendel

Mendel had no scientific training and knew nothing of what happened inside cells. When his findings were published in1866, they were ignored. Today, scientists recognize the importance of Mendel's idea. It is now called the **law of segregation**. Here is one way of expressing it:

Most cells have *two* code-carrying particles for each characteristic. When gametes (sex cells) are made, the particles get separated. This means that each gamete has only *one* code-carrying particle for each characteristic.

The diagram below also illustrates this law.

1 Why do you think scientists ignored Mendel's findings when they were first published?
2 What does the word 'segregation' mean? Do you think it is a good name for the law?
3 According to the law of segregation, how many code-carrying particles do most cells have for each characteristic?
4 According to the law of segregation, how many code-carrying particles do gametes have for each characteristic?

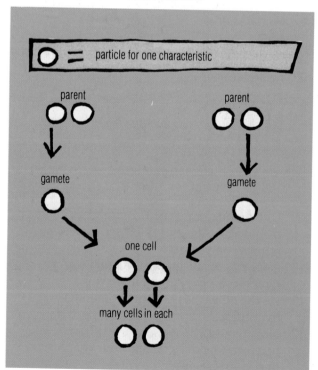

Chromosomes

To explain his results, Mendel suggested that there were tiny code-carrying particles in plants and other living things. But he had no direct evidence that these particles existed.

Today scientists can use powerful microscopes to study what happens inside the nucleus of a cell. They can see how some cells divide to form gametes (sex cells). The diagram on the right shows the main stages. This is one example of **cell division**.

In the nucleus, there are thin strands called **chromosomes**. These become visible just before the cell divides. To begin with, the chromosomes are single strands. But then they copy themselves so that two identical, linked strands are formed. Each strand is called a **chromatid**.

Most chromosomes are in pairs which match in size and shape. Every cell in the body has the same pairs of chromosomes.

5 Make a series of drawings to show what happens to one pair of chromosomes during the cell division shown.
6 Is the result similar to Mendel's ideas about code-carrying particles? If so, how?
7 How does the number of chromosomes in the original cell compare with the number of chromosomes in each gamete?
8 Is this what Mendel would have expected?

Genes

From the evidence they have seen, scientists think that chromosomes behave in a similar way to Mendel's code-carrying particles. However, humans need codes for thousands of characteristics. And there are only 23 pairs of chromosomes in a human cell.

9 Do you think that chromosomes could be Mendel's code-carrying particles? Explain your answer.

Scientists believe that there must be hundreds of code-carrying units in each chromosome. They now call them **genes**. The study of inherited characteristics is known as **genetics**.

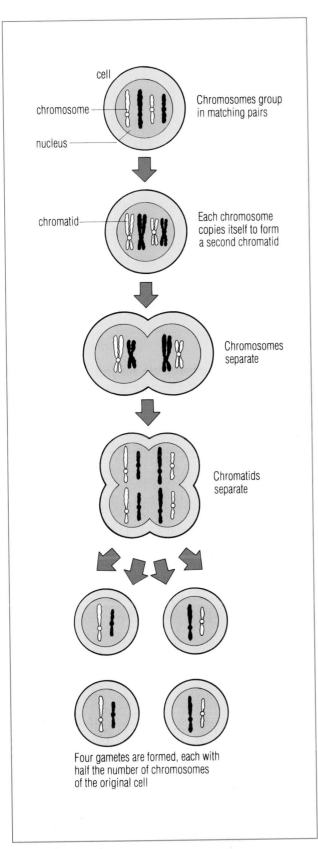

cell

chromosome

nucleus

Chromosomes group in matching pairs

chromatid

Each chromosome copies itself to form a second chromatid

Chromosomes separate

Chromatids separate

Four gametes are formed, each with half the number of chromosomes of the original cell

This is how a cell divides to form gametes (sex cells). It is called meiosis. Only a few of the chromosomes in the cell have been drawn. The two chromosomes in each pair are shown black and white so that you can tell them apart.

Words and meanings

Genes These are chemical codes for the characteristics of living things. There are hundreds of genes in each chromosome. Each gene deals with a single characteristic.

Alleles These are genes which deal with the same characteristic, for example: seed shape. A round-seed gene and a wrinkled-seed gene are alleles. Alleles are in matching positions along their chromosomes.

Homozygous This describes alleles which are the same. For example, a wrinkled-seed plant has two wrinkled-seed genes. These are homozygous.

Heterozygous This describes alleles which are different. For example, if a round-seed plant has one round-seed gene and one wrinkled-seed gene, the genes are heterozygous.

Dominant This describes a gene which can mask another one. For example, a round-seed gene masks a wrinkled-seed gene. So, the round-seed gene is dominant.

Recessive This describes the gene that is masked by the dominant gene. In the previous example, the wrinkled-seed gene is recessive because it is masked by the round-seed gene.

Meiosis This is the type of cell division in which gametes (sex cells) are formed. Meiosis only happens in cells of the organs that deal with reproduction.

Today, scientists have a range of words to describe the things that Mendel wrote about. You can see some of these words above.

Below, is a report on Mendel's work. Parts of it have been printed in *italics*.

10 Rewrite the report, replacing the words in italics with the words which scientists might use today.

"It seems that there are two *code-carrying particles* for each characteristic. These may be *the same*, or they may be *different*. If they are *different*, one will be *masked by the other* and will not affect what the organism looks like. When *the cell division which forms gametes* takes place, the two *code-carrying particles* get separated. As a result, the gametes each have half the number of *code-carrying particles* in the original cell."

Q 1.4 More about genes

Scientists think that genes are arranged on chromosomes rather like beads on a string. You can see their ideas in the diagram on the right. It shows a few of the genes in a pair of chromosomes from a human cell. The two chromosomes are identical in size and shape. Scientists call them a **homologous pair.** Genes which carry codes for the same characteristic (for example, hair colour) are in matching positions along the chromosomes. Here, the chromosomes are shown alongside each other. In a real cell, they only pair up at certain times.

1 When do chromosomes pair up?
2 What does the term 'homologous pair' mean?
3 What are alleles?
4 What two genes for hair colour are present?
5 What colour hair do you think the person will have?
6 What colour eyes do you think the person will have?
7 Which of the alleles are heterozygous?

Phenotypes and genotypes

A characteristic which you can see, like black hair or round seeds, is called a **phenotype** ('type of physical appearance'). The combination of genes which produces this characteristic is called a **genotype** ('type of genes'). For example, a round seed is a phenotype. Its genotype could be a dominant round-seed gene combined with a recessive wrinkled-seed gene. Coded information carried by genes is sometimes called the **genetic code**.

Look at the two pictures on the right.
8 Have any phenotypes changed? If so, how?
9 Have any genotypes changed? If so, how?

Look back to the photographs in spread Q1.1.
10 Which characteristics do you think are controlled by the genetic code?
11 Which characteristics are due to a phenotype which has been altered?
12 Which characteristics are inherited?

Sometimes, the environment can alter a phenotype.
13 Why was it important that Mendel grew all his plants in identical conditions?

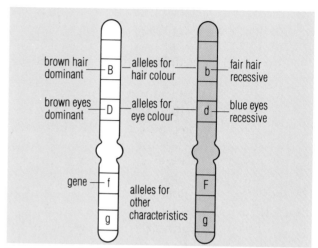

Homologous pair of chromosomes. The genes are indicated by letters. Dominant genes have a capital letter, recessive genes have a small letter.

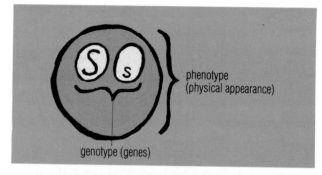

Before...............................and after

Not so simple

Not all characteristics are inherited as simply as those which Mendel investigated. For example, in red and white geraniums no gene is dominant or recessive. In a case like this, scientists say that the genes are **co-dominant**.

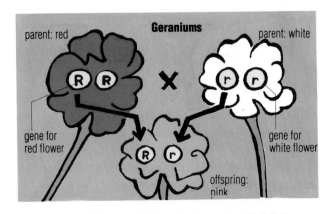

The diagram on the right shows one possible offspring if pure-breeding red and white geraniums are crossed. Here, the phenotype is a pink flower.

14 What is the genotype of the offspring?
15 Draw your own diagrams to show any other ways in which genes from parents could be passed on to the offspring.
16 What is the genotype of each offspring you have drawn?
17 What is the phenotype of each one?
18 Why would co-dominance have caused problems for Mendel if he had come across it in his experiments?

Many other characteristics are not inherited as simply as those which Mendel studied. Many are controlled by more than one pair of genes, so several combinations are possible.

Translating the code

Genes are made of a chemical known as **deoxyribose nucleic acid** (**DNA** for short). DNA molecules are made of tiny pieces of other chemicals joined together. Four of these are adenine, cytosine, guanine and thymine. They are called **organic bases** and usually known by their first letters **A**, **C**, **G** and **T**. They can be arranged in any order.

Characteristics like coat colour can be controlled by more than one pair of genes.

Scientists think that each group of three bases stands for a different 'word' of the genetic code. The different 'words' make the cell produce different **amino acids**, shown as symbols in the diagram on the right. Amino acids are used to build **proteins**. Living things, with their different characteristics, are partly made from proteins.

19 In the diagram, what would be the new sequence of symbols if the base marked * were lost?

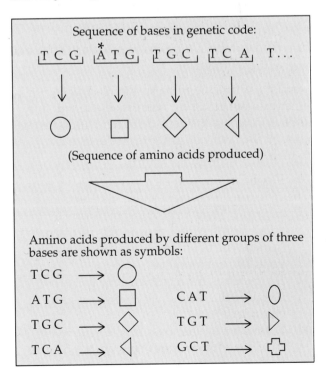

Did you know?

Everyone has a different genetic code, apart from identical twins, who have the same genetic code.

20 Are the phenotypes of identical twins the same?

137

Q 1.5 More about chromosomes

Most human cells have 23 pairs of chromosomes in the nucleus. But these only pair off during cell division.

1 Why must the chromosomes pair up?
2 In what ways are the members of a homologous pair the same?
3 In what ways are they different?

The chromosomes of pair 23 do not always appear to match each other. These are the **sex chromosomes**. They control whether a person is male or female. Females have two similar chromosomes, both called X. Males have one X and one Y chromosome. The diagram on the right shows how the chromosomes become separated when gametes are made.

4 How do chromosomes X and Y differ?
5 What sex will the baby be if a sperm with an X chromosome fertilizes the egg?
6 What sex will the baby be if a sperm with a Y chromosome fertilizes the egg?
7 What are the chances of the baby being a girl?

Genetic diseases

Some diseases are inherited. They are caused by genes. Sickle cell anaemia and haemophilia are two examples of genetic diseases.

8 Find out the symptoms of sickle cell anaemia and haemophilia.

Virtually all haemophilia sufferers are men. Scientists say that the disease is sex-linked. A mother can pass the gene on to her children even though she does not suffer from the disease herself. The mother is a **carrier**.

Haemophilia is caused by a rare, recessive gene. The diagram on the right shows its position on its chromosome. Most X chromosomes have a dominant, non-harmful gene in this position.

9 Which type of chromosome can carry the gene for haemophilia?
10 If a male has the recessive gene for haemophilia, why must it show up as a characteristic?
11 Why can a mother pass on the gene to her children without suffering from the disease herself?

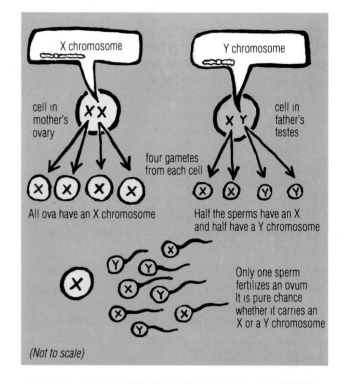

four gametes from each cell

All ova have an X chromosome

Half the sperms have an X and half have a Y chromosome

Only one sperm fertilizes an ovum It is pure chance whether it carries an X or a Y chromosome

(Not to scale)

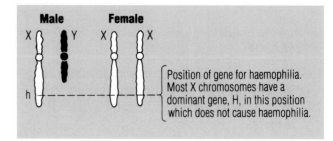

Queen Victoria was a carrier of the haemophilia gene. One of her sons and several of her grandsons and great-grandsons suffered from the disease.

Position of gene for haemophilia. Most X chromosomes have a dominant gene, H, in this position which does not cause haemophilia.

Looking at a karyogram

A **karyogram** is a display showing a complete set of chromosomes arranged in pairs. On the right is a karyogram of a child with Down's syndrome .

12 What sex is the child?

13 Is there anything unusual about any of the 'pairs'? If so, what?

Down's syndrome is caused by a gamete with one chromosome too many. At meiosis, a pair of chromosomes fails to segregate. Of the four gametes produced, two have two copies of one chromosome, and two have none at all.

14 Use words and diagrams to explain
  a what happens when chromosomes segregate normally.
  b what has happened if a child is born with Down's syndrome.

More and more cells

Once two gametes have joined, the one cell has to develop into a complete organism. It does this by producing more cells. The first cell grows and divides, forming two new cells. These grow and divide.... and so on. This type of cell division is called **mitosis**. The pictures on the right show what happens to the chromosomes during mitosis.

The first cell had all the genetic information needed to make a new organism. All the new cells have identical copies of this information. Their chromosomes are exactly the same as in the original cell.

Although all the cells in an organism have the same genetic code, they may have different jobs to do. Scientists think that parts of the code can be switched on or off. So liver cells have different parts of the code working than, say, skin cells or heart cells.

Meiosis and mitosis are different types of cell division.

15 Which type is responsible for producing more and more cells like the first one?

16 Which type is responsible for producing gametes (sex cells)?

17 How many chromosomes are there in a normal human cell which has been produced by mitosis?

18 How many chromosomes are there in a normal human cell which has been produced by meiosis?

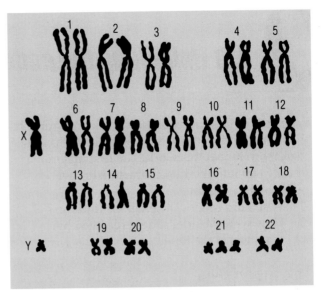

Karyogram of child with Down's syndrome

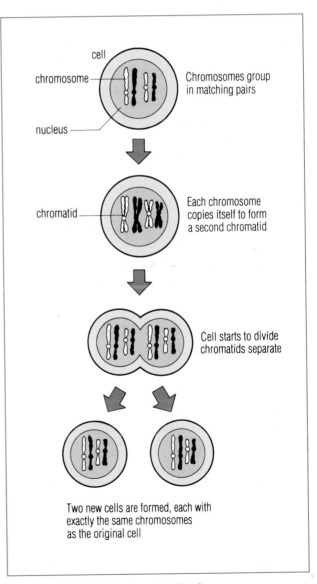

This type of cell division is called mitosis

Q 1.6 Unlocking the code

Scientists write reports of their work and publish them in scientific journals. Other scientists can then try to repeat this work. The first major findings about inherited characteristics were published by Mendel.

1 When did Mendel publish his findings?
2 How were Mendel's ideas received by scientists at the time?

Looking for clues

Nucleic acids are chemicals found in the nucleus of cells. By the early 1900s, scientists had worked out their main features. But it was not until 1944 that Oswald Avery, working in New York, discovered their true importance. He found that they carried genetic information. In his experiments, Avery used the simplest of all living organisms, bacteria. These can reproduce very rapidly. His results are illustrated in the top diagram on the right. Griffith had done similar experiments in London in the 1920s, but others had not realised their significance.

3 Why do you think Avery used bacteria for his experiments?
4 Why do Avery's results suggest that nucleic acids carry genetic information?

The nucleic acid which Avery investigated is called deoxyribose nucleic acid (DNA for short). At the time, scientists knew that its molecules were made from the types of chemicals shown in the second diagram on the right. The four bases are usually known by their first letters.

5 Until Avery's work, scientists thought that DNA molecules from different organisms all had their bases arranged in the same way. Why do you think that Avery's discovery made some scientists change their minds?

Between 1949 and 1951, Erwin Chargraff at Columbia University, USA, analysed the percentages of bases in the cells of different organisms. His results are shown on the right. He found links between some pairs of bases.

6 Can you see any links between the amounts of bases in the different organisms?
7 Do you think that the results support Avery's findings? If so, how?

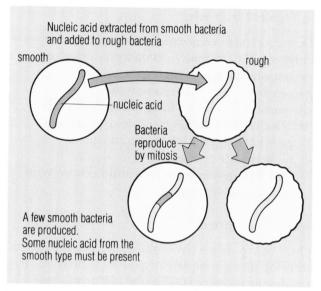

Nucleic acid extracted from smooth bacteria and added to rough bacteria

smooth — rough
nucleic acid
Bacteria reproduce by mitosis

A few smooth bacteria are produced. Some nucleic acid from the smooth type must be present

The results of Avery's experiments with bacteria

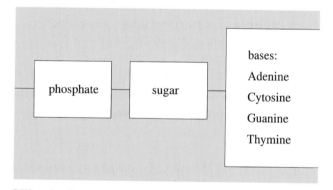

phosphate   sugar

bases:
Adenine
Cytosine
Guanine
Thymine

DNA molecules are made from these chemicals

Organism	% of each base in nucleic acid:			
	A	T	G	C
Escherichia coli (bacteria)	25.4	24.8	24.1	25.7
Wheat	26.8	28.0	23.2	22.7
Mouse	29.7	25.6	21.9	22.8
Pig: liver	29.4	29.7	20.5	20.5
thymus	30.0	28.9	20.4	20.7
spleen	29.6	29.2	20.4	20.8
Yeast	31.3	32.9	18.7	17.1

The problem solved

Scientists think that each chromosome contains one long, coiled-up molecule of DNA. This molecule may consist of millions of atoms. Today, scientists have a model to describe its structure. The ideas were first developed over forty years ago:

By1950, several teams of scientists were trying to work out the structure of DNA. In1952, Linus Pauling in the USA proposed one model: a spiral of three strands wrapped around each other. At the same time, Maurice Wilkins in London was using a technique called X-ray crystallography to study the structure of DNA. The X-ray photographs did not show the molecules. But they produced patterns which gave clues about their structure. These patterns were very difficult to interpret and Wilkins was unable to come up with any reasonable answers. However, Rosalind Franklin improved the X-ray techniques and obtained better photographs.

At Cambridge, James Watson and Francis Crick were also trying to build models of DNA molecules. In 1953, with the help of Rosalind Franklin's improved X-ray photographs, they proposed a new structure for the DNA molecule. It was a shape which they called a **double helix**: two chains twisting around each other rather like a spiral staircase. This is the model that scientists use today. You can see part of it in the diagram on the right.

Watson and Crick also suggested how DNA can make identical copies of itself. The double helix parts down the middle, rather like a zip. New 'pieces' of chemicals become attached to the two halves, so that each becomes a complete double helix. In 1958, Meselson and Stahl in California obtained experimental results which supported this model.

8 How does the Watson-Crick model of DNA differ from the Pauling model?

9 What are the cross-links (the 'rungs') of the double helix made of?

10 The bases will only fit together in certain pairs. What are these pairs?

11 How do you think Chargraff's results on the opposite page helped Crick and Watson develop their model?

12 List the main scientists on these pages, the dates of their work, what they did and the discoveries they made.

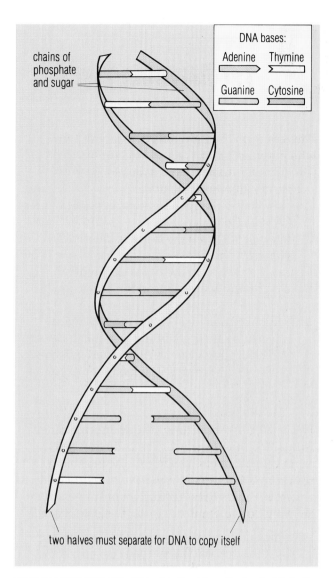

Part of a DNA molecule. The structure is called a double helix

Working as scientists

In 1962, Watson and Crick were awarded a Nobel Prize for their work. Four years earlier, Rosalind Franklin had died of cancer at the age of 37, probably from the effects of radiation. Her notes show that she was very close to finding the structure of DNA. Without her X-ray photographs Watson and Crick might never have solved the problem. Yet she was given little credit for her work. Watson wrote that he realised 'the struggles an intelligent woman faces to be accepted by a scientific world which often regards women as mere diversions from serious thinking'.

13 What do you think Watson meant by this?

14 Why do you think that there are far fewer female scientists than male ones?

15 What could be done to make science a more attractive career for women?

1.7 Matching up

The report on the right tells the story of twins who grew up apart.

1. What has to happen inside a mother for identical twins to be made?
2. What has to happen for non-identical twins to be made?
3. In what ways are the twins in the article similar?
4. In what ways are the twins different?
5. Do you think the twins in the article are identical?
6. Which of the twins' characteristics were affected by their genotype (genetic make-up)?
7. Which of their characteristics were affected by the environments in which they grew up?

Attack and defence

The cells of all organisms have chemicals called **antigens** on their surface. The code for these chemicals is carried by some of the organism's genes. So every person will have different antigens, unless they have an identical genotype.

8. What people will have identical genotypes?

Sometimes, 'foreign' antigens may get into our bodies, for example: the antigens on microbes. However our bodies produce their own chemicals called **antibodies** which attack and destroy these antigens.

9. How could foreign antigens get into our bodies?
10. How do our bodies usually respond?

Transplants

Sometimes, a seriously ill patient may be given an organ transplant. The transplanted organ usually comes from someone who has recently died. It will not be an exact match for the patient, but it must have very similar antigens or the patient's body will reject it. Bone marrow or a kidney can be donated by someone who is still living. Usually, this is a person in the same family.

11. What is an 'organ transplant'?
12. What organs have you heard of that can be transplanted?
13. Why can a kidney come from a donor who is still living?

The twin he never knew

Last weekend, a local builder, Malcolm Pratt, met the twin brother he did not know he had until seven weeks ago. Recently, Malcolm found he had been adopted as a baby. While trying to trace his real parents, he discovered that he had a twin. His twin's adoptive parents had moved to live in South Africa when he was three. His brother, Peter, arrived in London last week.

"I wouldn't have recognised him," said Malcolm. "Friends say his nose and eyes look like mine, but his skin is darker and his hair is much fairer". "It's because of the sunshine in South Africa," said Peter. "Last time I was in England for some time, my hair became darker." Both brothers have a small birth mark on one arm and both are 1.91 metres tall. However Peter weighs 8 kilograms more. "It's because I sit at a desk all day," said Peter, who is a bank clerk.

The brothers are looking forward to hill-walking together, which they both enjoy. They are trying to arrange visits to the theatre though this may be difficult. "I like comedies, but Malcolm prefers serious stuff," said Peter. "I hope to take him to the opera," said Malcolm. "He says he's never been before, but I really enjoy it."

Girl donates kidney to her twin

For the second time in just over a year, the village of Newport is celebrating the success of an operation where a patient received a transplant donated by a member of their family. Sari Brittan has just received a kidney from her twin sister, Pragnya. "Although we have two kidneys, we can manage quite well with one," explained their doctor. "We had not been able to find a kidney from a suitable donor, and Pragnya offered one of hers. In fact, she was the best donor because she was an identical twin."

Last year, a father donated bone marrow to his son, Irvin. Irvin's body had rejected two previous transplants, so doctors turned to the family. "Members of the family are often the best donors", said Dr. Russell. "We tested several of Irvin's family and found his father was the best match. This reduced the chance of Irvin rejecting the new bone marrow.

Read the report on the opposite page about the girl who donated one of her kidneys to her twin sister.

14 Why do you think members of the same family are often the best donors of bone marrow or a kidney?

15 Why do you think an identical twin is the best donor of all?

Blood groups and transfusions

Blood has far fewer antigens than organs like the heart or kidneys. The two most important are called **A antigens** and **B antigens**.

Human blood can be divided into four main groups, called **A**, **B**, **AB** and **O**. The group depends on the antigens present. The antigens could be A, or B, or both, or neither. This is shown in the first table on the right.

Blood also contains antibodies. The ones in the table are shown as **anti-A** and **anti-B**. An anti-A antibody will attack an A antigen.

It is possible to 'transplant' blood from one person to another. This is called a transfusion. A patient must not be given blood with antigens which their own antibodies would attack. The antibodies would make the red cells in the blood clump together.

Discuss and answer the following questions with your group:

16 Why do you think blood transfusions were perfected many years before organ transplants?

17 Why could an incorrect transfusion make red blood cells clump together?

18 Why would it be dangerous if red blood cells clumped together?

19 Look at the statements on the right. Say whether you agree or disagree with each one. Explain your reasons.

20 Why can a person with group O donate blood to all other blood groups?

21 Which group can receive blood from any other blood group?

In humans, there are *three* possible genes for blood group. They are called A, B and O. Of these, A and B are co-dominant (equally dominant). Both are dominant to O. Cells contain only *two* of these genes.

22 Copy and complete the table on the right to show the six possible combinations of genes, and the blood group given by each.

Receiver's blood			Donor's blood
Group	A or B antigens present	anti-A or anti-B antibodies present	Groups that will react with receiver's blood
A	A	anti-B	B and AB
B	B	anti-A	A and AB
AB	A and B	-	-
O	-	anti-A, anti-B	A, B and AB

Blood cannot have antibodies for its own antigens. The antigens would be attacked!   X

In a transfusion, you have to be given blood of exactly the same group as your own.   Y

Each blood group has antibodies for those antigens which it does *not* have.   Z

Pairs of genes	Blood group	Pairs of genes	Blood group
A A	A	B O	
A O	A	O O	
B B		A B	A B

1.8 Breeding the best

Look at the first two photographs (**A** and **B**) on the right. Each shows an animal which has been carefully bred so that its special characteristics are the best possible.

1 What are the special characteristics of each animal?

2 How do you think breeders select animals to breed from?

3 What other desirable characteristics might these animals have which cannot be seen in a photograph? List your ideas.

Breeds and cross-breeds

Animals like dogs and horses have been bred in many different varieties. These different varieties are called **breeds**.

Mongrels are dogs which do not belong to any particular breed. They are examples of **cross-breeds**. Most mongrels are the result of a chance meeting between two dogs: their parents have not been carefully chosen. Mongrels may have characteristics from several different breeds.

4 Why might a mongrel show characteristics from more than two breeds of dog?

5 Look at the mongrel in the bottom photograph. What characteristics of other breeds can you see in it? (You may need help from a dog owner to answer this!)

Animal breeders

Thousands of years ago, the ancestors of today's cows, sheep, pigs and other farm animals wandered wild over the country. When people grew tired of hunting for food, they started to capture animals like these and control them in herds. To begin with, they chose the animals which were easiest to capture and control. Later, they bred animals for certain characteristics, such as tender meat. This led to many different breeds.

6 What characteristics do you think animal breeders would have wanted to develop in their cows, sheep and pigs? List your ideas for each type of animal.

7 How would breeders have made sure that a particular characteristic was passed on to future generations?

Mongrel

Preserving rare breeds

Many breeds of farm animal have died out, because their characteristics are no longer in demand. As their genes cannot be remade, they have been lost forever. Nowadays, farmers try to preserve breeds which are close to dying out. They do this partly to save the genes. For example, if disease struck a common breed, all the animals might die. However, if a rare breed has genes which give it a high resistance to the disease, it could be used to improve the first breed. The photograph on the right shows one example of a rare breed of sheep.

8 If a breed dies out, what happens to the genes for its characteristics?

9 Why is it important to preserve rare breeds of farm animal?

10 How can an animal breeder use one breed to improve another?

Cutting and grafting

Plants are also bred by humans. Not all plants are grown from seed. Sometimes, cuttings are taken.

11 How will the genes of a cutting compare with the genes of the original plant?

A fruit tree raised from seed differs considerably from the 'mother' tree.

12 Where does a seed get its genes from?

13 Why will a fruit tree not be identical to the 'mother' tree?

The only certain way of keeping a variety of fruit going is by **grafting**. This is one of the oldest methods of breeding. The diagram on the right shows how it may be done. A piece of shoot called a **scion** is taken from the variety of tree that is wanted. The shoot is then grafted onto **rootstock** (the roots and part of the stem) of a different variety.

14 Are any gametes (sex cells) combined as a result of grafting?

15 What is 'rootstock'?

16 Where do the genes for the future fruit come from?

17 Where do the genes for the main body of the tree come from?

Read the advice from a gardening book on the right.

18 How can the same variety of fruit grow on different varieties of tree?

19 What are the advantages of growing fruit by this method?

Rare breed: this Dartmoor Greyface sheep was reared at the Cotswold Farm Park in Gloucestershire

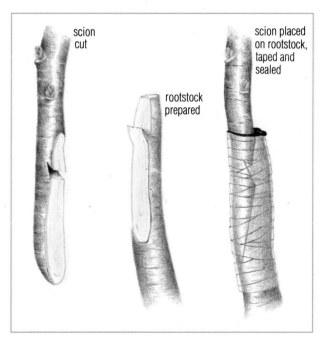

scion cut

rootstock prepared

scion placed on rootstock, taped and sealed

Grafting onto rootstock

When buying a fruit tree, tell the staff at the nursery about the type of soil and growing conditions it will have. Also tell them what form of tree you would like, for example, whether it should be tall or short, bushy or non-bushy. They should then be able to provide you with a tree of suitable rootstock.

Tulip bulbs were introduced to Holland in the 16th century. Bright colours were developed early in the 17th century and dark purples by the end of the 19th century. But no one thought that a black tulip would ever be produced. People trying to breed black tulips used similar methods to Mendel's. They transferred pollen to stigmas with a tiny brush. Later, the flowers were dried, and their seeds collected and planted. After many years of pollination experiments, the first black tulip grew from a seed. This was in 1986.

1 What does pollen contain?
2 If a tulip seed is produced as a result of cross-pollination, where does its genetic information come from?

Once the first black tulip had appeared, more plants were wanted. But these were not grown from seed. They were produced by taking tiny bulbs from the main bulb.

3 If tiny bulbs are taken from a main bulb, why does this ensure that genetically identical plants are produced?
4 If you pollinated one black tulip from another, why could you not guarantee that the offspring would be black?
5 Why do you think that growers did not expect to grow more black tulips by using seeds from the first one?

Cloning

Cox's Orange Pippins are a popular type of apple. All are descended from one seedling which was found in a hedgerow. Cuttings were taken from the original tree to make sure that new trees were genetically identical to the original. Scientists say that the new trees were all **clones** of the original.

Today, cloning is commonly used for producing large numbers of genetically identical plants. Growing parts of a plant are taken and put in nutrients. Chemicals called **hormones** are added to encourage more stems or roots to grow.

6 What are 'clones'?
7 Describe what is happening at each stage of the diagram on the right.
8 What type of cell division is taking place to produce the new plants?

Cross-breeding has produced many different colours of tulip.

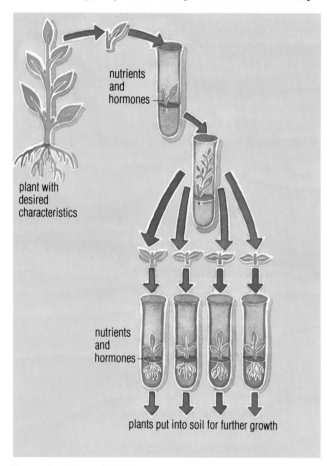

plant with desired characteristics

nutrients and hormones

nutrients and hormones

plants put into soil for further growth

The main stages of cloning

The same or different?

On a plant, chemicals can be used to make a group of cells divide rapidly. The growing clump of cells is called a **callus**. Clones can be made from it. The cells in a callus divide so rapidly that errors sometimes occur when the chromosomes copy themselves. This changes the genetic code. It is an advantage if a breeder is looking for variation, but a disadvantage if genetically identical plants are required.

9 What are the advantages of a breeder producing large numbers of genetically identical plants? List your ideas.

10 What are the disadvantages of a breeder producing large numbers of genetically identical plants?

Genetic engineering

Scientists have discovered how to alter some of the genes in plants, animals and bacteria. This is called **genetic engineering**. It can be used to give organisms particular characteristics which the scientists want.

In genetic engineering, a piece of DNA is transferred from one organism to another. There, it combines with the second organism's DNA. The piece of DNA transferred is usually a single gene. It can be transferred from one species to another, for example: from humans across to bacteria.

The diagram on the right shows how a human gene for making insulin can be transferred into a bacterium. A special molecule called a **vector molecule** is used to carry the gene to its new cell. Bacteria, genetically engineered in this way, can produce insulin very rapidly. Insulin is vital for the treatment of diabetes.

The five stages in transferring a gene are listed on the right, but not in the right order.

11 Put the five stages into the correct order.

Look again at the diagram on this page.

12 Draw your own larger version of this diagram. Write additional notes around it to describe what is happening.

Genetic engineering is a recent discovery.

13 Before genetic engineering was developed, how did breeders introduce a desired gene into a population?

14 Why is genetic engineering an advantage over this?

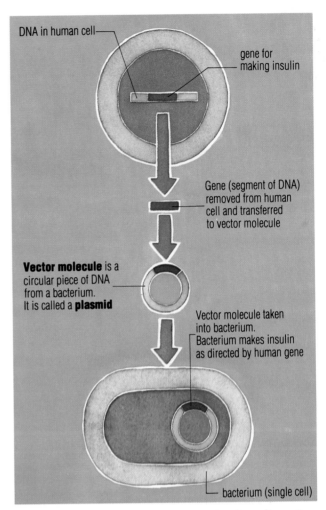

DNA in human cell

gene for making insulin

Gene (segment of DNA) removed from human cell and transferred to vector molecule

Vector molecule is a circular piece of DNA from a bacterium. It is called a **plasmid**

Vector molecule taken into bacterium. Bacterium makes insulin as directed by human gene

bacterium (single cell)

An example of genetic engineering: transferring a piece of human DNA to a bacterium (a single 'bacteria').

Five stages in transferring a gene
(*not* in the correct order)

A Join the gene up with the vector molecule.

B Treat the receiver cell so that it is ready for the new DNA.

C Locate the desired gene in the donor organism.

D Select only those cells which have taken up the 'foreign' DNA.

E Cut the gene to be transferred and make it join to the vector molecule.

Single molecules are too small to be dealt with individually, so the above stages are carried out using chemical techniques.

Read the reports on this page and answer the questions.

Extra-special event

For Jane and Malcolm Hutchinson, the birth of a son was an extra-special event. At one time, it seemed impossible that Jane would ever become pregnant. Jane has blocked oviducts. Malcolm had a vesectomy five years ago following the birth of his children in a previous marriage.

The couple have been attending a fertility clinic where some of Jane's ova (eggs) were removed in an operation and frozen. Later, the ova were mixed with sperms donated to a sperm bank. Surgeons selected a fertilized ovum and implanted it in Jane's uterus where it developed into the baby. 'We couldn't choose the sperm donor,' said Jane. 'I'm hoping that it was a professional footballer,' joked Malcolm. 'Our baby might become a good player!'

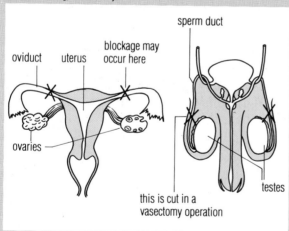

Freaks on the farm

People in Ledmore are claiming that a nearby experimental farm is creating genetic freaks. The farm is producing top quality calves from a herd of poor quality cows, but the cows are not the genetic mothers. Scientists are taking ove (eggs) from top quality cows elsewhere, storing them frozen, and then mixing them with sperms taken from prize-winning bulls. This is producing embryos which are implanted into the cows, where they develop until they are born.

A spokesperson for the farm said: 'We are not breeding freaks, and the process does not harm the cows. We are producing better cattle that give more milk from smaller pastures. This frees land for other purposes.' The protestors do not agree. 'The process is irresponsible and unnecessary,' said one. 'Farmers are already producing far more milk than is needed. The cows are not allowed to breed naturally, their genes will be lost and this may cause problems in the future.'

1 Why would blocked oviducts or a vasectomy normally prevent a couple from having children?

2 Malcolm joked about the donated sperms. But do you think that having a baby by the method described was an easy decision for the couple to make?

3 With your group, make a list of the arguments for and against having a baby like this.

4 What were the reasons given for producing cattle in the way described? What other reasons can you think of?

5 What reasons can you think of for *not* using this process on cattle?

6 What do you think the protestor meant when he said 'Their genes will be lost'? Was he correct in saying this? Explain your answer.

Now compare the two reports.

7 In what ways are the scientific ideas used similar? In what ways are they different?

8 Do you think it is right that doctors and scientists have been allowed to develop these methods?

Research news

The reports on this page describe some of the results of genetic research. Read and discuss them with your group. For each report:

9 Descibe what each gene does.

10 Decide whether you think that the research is of any value to humanity.

11 Decide whether you think that there are moral reasons for stopping the research.

D Maize (corn) usually lacks two amino acids essential to humans. 200 million people in the world rely on maize for their food, and so risk being short of these amino acids. In 1963, a new strain of maize was discovered. It possessed the two amino acids, but had many undesirable qualities as well. Mexican scientists crossed, selected and re-bred the maize until, in1990, they produced a strain which had all the qualities of the traditional maize, plus the two amino acids.

A In Scotland, a flock of sheep has become a living 'factory' for making Factor IX, a substance needed by haemophilia sufferers because it helps blood clot. Factor IX is normally only found in human blood. But scientists have located the gene responsible for making Factor IX in humans and have put it into the fertilized eggs of sheep. As a result, they now have sheep which produce Factor IX in their milk.

B The human body normally makes its own insulin, but diabetics need an external supply. Until recently, most of the insulin needed by diabetics was extracted from the pancreas of dead cows. Today, the gene which controls insulin production can be transferred from human cells to bacteria. The genetically-altered bacteria are used to produce insulin in huge fermentation tanks.

E Petunia plants have been given extra genes to help them withstand the effects of a weedkiller. The genes are responsible for producing an enzyme vital to plants. The weedkiller works by destroying this enzyme, but petunias with the extra genes can make enough of the enzyme to survive.

C As a result of genetic research, scientists can now identify the genes which cause muscular dystrophy and cystic fibrosis. If a woman is carrying an embryo which is at risk, she can be offered an abortion.

Q 2.1 Evolving ideas

Evolution is about changing. For example, cars, bicycles and other things designed by humans have changed over the years.

1 Choose cars or bicycles. List the changes that have happened to their design. Why do you think these changes have happened.

Then and now

Some animals and plants from the past no longer exist today. Some of today's animals and plants did not seem to exist in ancient times. And some look very different from those of previous generations.

2 Why do you think that animals and plants have changed over the centuries?

Modern giraffes have longer necks than those of a million years ago. The giraffes in the pictures have their own explanations!

3 Which pair of giraffes do you agree with?

There have been many explanations for the variety of living things on Earth and the similarities between groups. There are four statements about these below, but the beginnings and endings have been muddled up.

4 Decide what you think each of the following means:

descended   ancestor
evolution   survival of the fittest

5 Match up the beginnings and endings below to make four complete statements.
6 Which statements do you agree with?
7 List your group's ideas about evolution. Which do you agree with? Which do you disagree with? Which are you not sure about?

Beginnings...	...and endings
A Humans have descended from the apes...	**E** and have not changed since being created.
B Humans and all animals and plants were created by God...	**F** which is why we are similar to monkeys.
C All mammals have similar characteristics...	**G** and reproduce as well as strong, healthy ones.
D It is survival of the fittest. Weak organisms do not survive...	**H** because they have all developed from the same ancestor millions of years ago.

The evolution of life

All living things on Earth probably developed from the same simple beginnings. This is the idea which scientists call evolution. It cannot be proved, but most scientists think that there is enough evidence to support it. Use the chart below to help you answer the following:

8 What needed to happen to the Earth before life could begin?

9 Which stages took place in water?

10 Name five different jobs done by specialized cells.

11 What two changes had to happen to animals before they could live on land?

Look at the statements on the right.

12 Which ideas do you agree with? Why?

13 Which ideas do you disagree with? Why?

A: In millions of years' time, today's fish will have developed into humans.

B: I agree. But apes will develop into humans sooner because they are more like us.

C: I disagree with you both. Neither will turn into humans. I think that the animals of a particular group may change over millions of years, but one group will not change into another group.

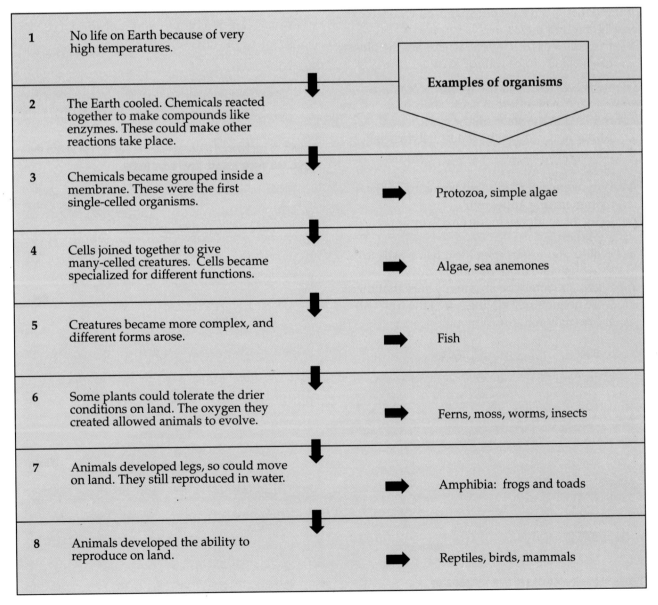

#	Description		Examples of organisms
1	No life on Earth because of very high temperatures.		
2	The Earth cooled. Chemicals reacted together to make compounds like enzymes. These could make other reactions take place.		
3	Chemicals became grouped inside a membrane. These were the first single-celled organisms.	→	Protozoa, simple algae
4	Cells joined together to give many-celled creatures. Cells became specialized for different functions.	→	Algae, sea anemones
5	Creatures became more complex, and different forms arose.	→	Fish
6	Some plants could tolerate the drier conditions on land. The oxygen they created allowed animals to evolve.	→	Ferns, moss, worms, insects
7	Animals developed legs, so could move on land. They still reproduced in water.	→	Amphibia: frogs and toads
8	Animals developed the ability to reproduce on land.	→	Reptiles, birds, mammals

Q 2.2 Looking for evidence

Scientists have developed their ideas on evolution by collecting evidence about animals and plants which once lived on Earth.

Looking at fossils

The remains of nearly all the animals and plants which lived millions of years ago have long since vanished. However, a few were preserved by mud or other fragments which settled in layers around them. Later, the layers became sedimentary rocks, and the animal and plant remains became fossils. Today, a tiny proportion of these fossils have become exposed where people can find them.

1 In a series of rock layers, where are the oldest fossils likely to be found? Why?

Scientists have counted the numbers of fossils found in rocks of different ages. Their findings are summarized in the chart on the right.

2 About how old are the oldest fish fossils?
3 About how old are the oldest mammal fossils?
4 Why were fish fossils still being made when mammals first appeared?
5 Does the evidence in the chart support evolution?
6 Would you expect the oldest fish fossils to show fish like those of today?
7 Scientists cannot be absolutely sure that there were no mammals living when the first fish appreared on Earth. Why not?

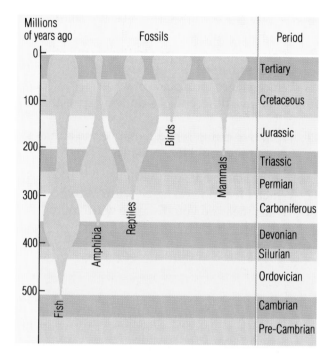

Fossils of backboned animals found in rocks: the wider the strip, the more fossils have been found.

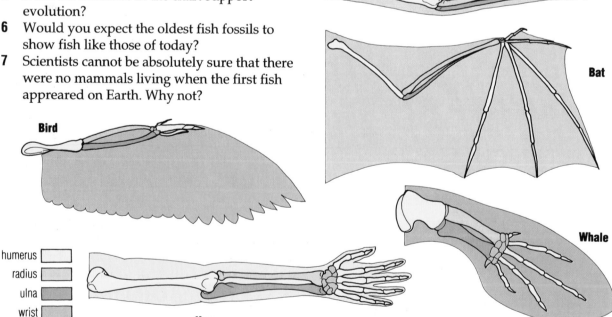

Bones of the front limbs of five vertebrates

Looking at limbs

Animals with backbones are called **vertebrates**. The diagram at the bottom of the opposite page shows the bones of the front limbs of five vertebrates.

8 What would each animal use the limb for?

9 In what ways are these five limbs similar?

10 Do you think that these animals could have evolved from a common ancestor? Explain your answer.

More evidence?

By studying fossils from different ages of rock, scientists have tried to work out what horses have looked like in the past. You can see some of their ideas on the right.

11 List all the changes you can see in the horses at the different stages shown.

Read the following information:

- If an animal is **adapted** to its environment, this means that it has all the features needed to live in it.
- No two animals in a group are exactly alike. So some are slightly better adapted to their environment than others. These are the ones which are most likely to survive and breed.
- Over millions of years, an animal's environment can change. 60 million years ago, some of the countryside was marshy, with lots of small trees which offered hiding places for small animals. By one million years ago, the environment had dried out. Trees had been replaced by grassland. This offered fewer hiding places.
- If an animal cannot hide, it must run fast to escape predators (hunting animals). It has more chance of escaping if it has a good view of the countryside.
- Flat feet reduce the risks of sinking into soft ground. But, an animal with flat feet will find it difficult to run fast.

Use the information above to help you answer the following:

12 What would have happened to horses with narrow feet in marshy land?

13 What would have happened to horses that could only run slowly on dry ground?

14 Why do you think modern horses look different from those of millions of years ago? See if you can use your ideas about inheritance to answer this question.

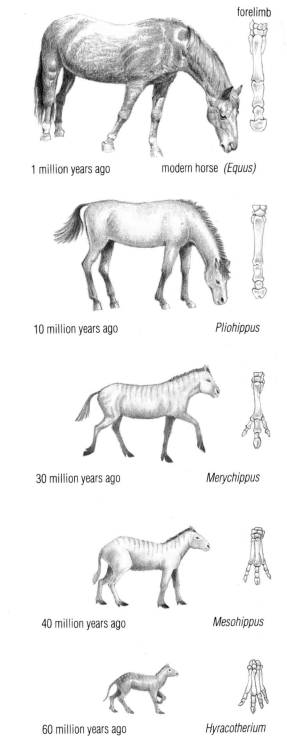

forelimb

1 million years ago   modern horse *(Equus)*

10 million years ago   *Pliohippus*

30 million years ago   *Merychippus*

40 million years ago   *Mesohippus*

60 million years ago   *Hyracotherium*

Today, most scientists accept that evolution has taken place in horses, but some are doubtful about the links between the horses in the chart. They say that there is no evidence to show that each horse found as a fossil was a descendant of the one beneath it.

15 What other explanation could there be for finding fossils showing different features in different levels of rock?

Charles Darwin was one of the first scientists to explain why evolution might take place. This was in 1858. He based his ideas on observations made while sailing round the world in *HMS Beagle* in the 1830s.

The theory of natural selection

While on the Galapagos Islands in the South Pacific, Darwin studied the finches living on each island. He noticed differences in their beaks. The diagram below shows how Darwin thought these differences could be explained.

1 Why do many finches die when they are young?
2 What is meant by 'compete for food'?
3 What advantage did the insect-eating finches have?
4 What might have caused the variation in the finches' beaks in the first place?

5 What would happen if a few finches had a variation to their beaks that allowed them to feed on buds and fruit?

Darwin's ideas are now known as the **theory of natural selection**:
- In any group of organisms, individuals are different: there are variations.
- Some variations give an advantage in the struggle for survival.
- Only the survivors reproduce and pass on their characteristics to their offspring.
- As a result, organisms slowly evolve so that they become adapted to their environment.

6 Natural selection is sometimes called 'the survival of the fittest'. Do you think this is a suitable name'?
7 In the diagram, which items are facts, and which are ideas to explain the facts?

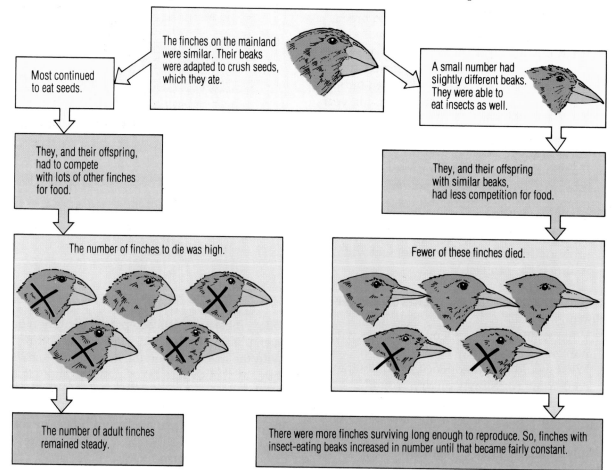

A changing environment

Peppered moths live in woodlands and are eaten by birds. There are both light and dark varieties. In the 1850s, dark moths were very rare. But then soot from factories started to blacken tree trunks. By 1895, 98% of the peppered moths in Manchester were dark.

8 On a light tree trunk, which variety of peppered moth was likely to survive long enough to reproduce?

9 When tree trunks became blackened, which variety had the best chance of survival?

10 Why did dark moths become more common than light ones in polluted areas?

The peppered moth population changed because its environment changed. But a few dark moths had always existed because they had inherited a gene for dark colour.

11 Inheriting the gene for dark colour only became an advantage when the environment changed. Why?

12 What might have happened if the environment had not changed?

Mutations

For natural selection to occur, there must be variations within a group. Variations can be caused by changes to the genetic code carried by DNA. The changes are called **mutations**. Some happen spontaneously, others are caused by chemicals or by radiation. Most are harmful, but some can be helpful.

13 Why are harmful mutations less likely to be passed on to future generations?

14 Why might a helpful mutation be hidden until the environment changes?

The diagram below shows part of a DNA base code before a mutation has occured.

15 Write down the new code if the base marked * is lost. Mark in the new triplets.

16 How many triplets are unchanged?

Sequence of bases in genetic code:

⌐A T C⌐ ⌐G T T̊⌐ ⌐A A C⌐ ⌐T G C⌐ T . . .

triplet
(group
of 3
bases)

Part of a DNA base code

Which peppered moth is better adapted to its environment?

An alternative view

Before Darwin, Lamarck had come up with a different explanation for evolution. This was in 1809. His idea was that, during its daily life, an organism can develop the characteristics which it needs: strong arms for example. These characteristics may then be passed on to its offspring.

When giraffes feed, they have to stretch to reach the higher parts of trees and bushes.

17 How would Lamarck have explained the long necks of modern giraffes?

18 How would Darwin have explained them?

19 Whose ideas do you think Mendel would have agreed with?

3.1 Keeping healthy

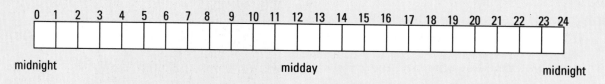

Most people can usually decide what they should do to help keep themselves healthy. But doing something about it is much harder!

1 Copy the chart above and shade in the things you did yesterday. Use different colours for *eating, sleeping, sitting down, exercising* and other things you can think of. Make a key to show what each colour means.

2 Discuss which things were benefiting your health, and which things may have been harming it.

3 Describe any ways in which the pattern of your activities might be different on other days.

4 In your group, 'brainstorm' words which you connect with a healthy life style. Remember to list these words as you think of them.

5 Now do the same for words which you connect with an unhealthy lifestyle.

6 In each of the lists you brainstormed, put the words into groups. The groups should show which words refer to the following things: *diet, exercise, physical health* and *mental health*. The same word may be in more than one group.

7 In one sentence, try to give a definition of 'being healthy'.

Effects of exercise

Physical exercise can be judged by its effects on *stamina, suppleness* and *strength*.

8 Discuss what the words in italics mean. Then decide what you could do to make improvements to each one. Remember to list your ideas.

9 Copy and complete the table below to show how you would rate the effects of the different types of activity.

Activity	Stamina	Suppleness	Strength
badminton	• •	• • •	• •
disco dancing	• • •	• • • •	•
squash	• • •	• • •	• •
climbing stairs	• • •	•	• •
digging garden	• • •	• •	• • • •
football	• • •	• • •	• • •
swimming (hard)	• • • •	• • • •	• • • •
cycling (hard)	• • • •	• •	• • •
cricket			
netball			
golf			
hockey			
gymnastics			
jogging			
tennis			
weightlifting			

• = No real benefit
• • = Good effect
• • • = Very good effect
• • • • = Excellent effect

Health hazards

Although we may try to keep healthy, we often face health hazards in our environment. There are some examples in the photographs on this page.

10 What do you think is meant by 'health hazards'?

11 Write down the health hazards you can see in each photograph and the ways in which they may harm someone's health. For each one, discuss what could be done by individuals or by governments to reduce the problem.

3.2 The breath of life

The food you eat contains stored energy. But the energy is of no use to you until it is released from the food. The energy is released by chemical reactions in the cells of your body. The process is called **respiration**. It is summarized on the right. In some ways, it is rather like burning but without the flames. For example, stored energy is released when coal is burned.

1 What gas is needed for burning?
2 What gas is needed for respiration?
3 What gas is produced by burning?
4 What gas is produced by respiration?

Your heart and lungs work together to supply the cells of your muscles and other parts of the body with the gas they need for respiration. All your cells have a flow of blood very close to them.

5 What gas is needed by your muscles?
6 What gas does blood collect from your lungs?
7 What gas is produced by your muscles?
8 What gas is removed from the blood in your lungs?
9 How does blood get to the lungs?

Inside the lungs

Air passes into the lungs through the **trachea** (windpipe). You can see this on the right. The trachea branches into two, then branches many times more into very tiny air tubes with swellings at their ends. The swellings are surrounded by tiny blood tubes called **capillaries**.

10 What are the tiny swellings called?
11 The walls between the air sacs and the blood tubes are so thin that gases can seep through. Why do you think this is?
12 Why is it better to have lots of tiny air tubes in the lungs rather than a few large ones?

The bottom diagram on the right shows you what happens to air in the lungs. Air is a mixture of gases including oxygen and carbon dioxide.

13 Where is the concentration of oxygen higher, in the air sacs or in the blood?
14 Where is the concentration of carbon dioxide higher, in the air sacs or in the blood?
15 Which way does the oxygen move?
16 Which way does the carbon dioxide move?

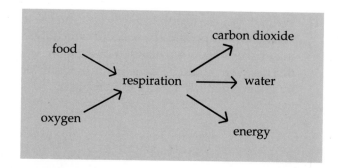

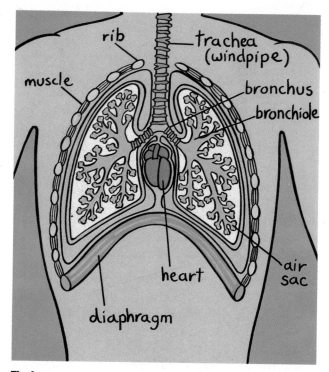

The lungs

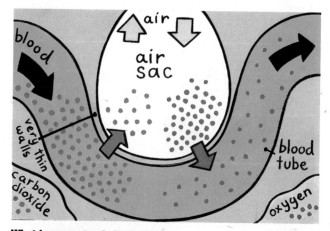

What happens to air in the lungs

Did you know?

Cystic fibrosis is a genetic illness which causes mucus to be produced so that the lungs fill up. Sufferers need regular physiotherapy to help them cough so that mucus is squeezed from their lungs.

The colour of blood

Oxygenated blood is a slightly different colour from deoxygenated blood. The photograph on the right shows what happens when oxygen is bubbled through one sample of blood and carbon dioxide is bubbled through another. To begin with, both samples of blood contained almost no gas.

17 What do you think the terms 'oxygenated blood' and 'deoxygenated blood' mean?

18 In the photograph, what is the difference in colour between the two types of blood?

19 In the photograph, which experiment represents what happens in the lungs? What does the other experiment represent?

Janine's teacher bubbled oxygen into blood that had carbon dioxide in it. The blood changed to a redder colour! Some of the class were surprised, but Janine had expected this to happen.

20 Can you explain why it happened?

The effects of smoking

A doctor wanted to encourage some of her patients to give up smoking. She decided to show them an experiment. First, she bubbled some oxygen through a sample of deoxygenated blood. Next, she bubbled some cigarette smoke through another sample of deoxygenated blood, then she bubbled some oxygen through it as before. This time, the blood took longer to turn red.

21 What effect did the cigarette smoke have on the blood?

The poster on the right was used in an anti-smoking campaign. Tar from cigarettes gets into the lungs of smokers.

22 Which parts of the lungs do you think tar will settle in?

23 Use your knowledge of the lungs and the effects of cigarette smoke to explain why many smokers complain of being 'out of breath'.

24 Make a leaflet giving smokers information about what happens to blood when it passes through their lungs and the effects that smoking can have.

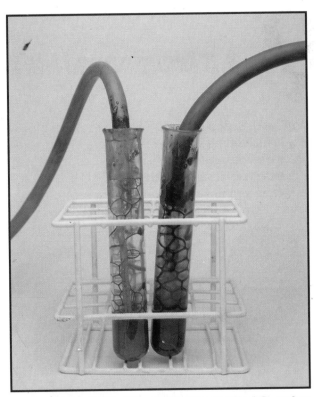

Oxygen is being bubbled through the blood on the left, carbon dioxide through the blood on the right.

No wonder smokers cough.

The tar and discharge that collects in the lungs of an average smoker.

HEALTH EDUCATION AUTHORITY

This poster shows the tar and discharge that can collect in the lungs of a smoker.

3.3 Blood round the body

With your group, discuss these ideas about blood.
1 Which of the statements
   a do you agree with?
   b do you disagree with?
   c are you not sure about?

Blood goes from the heart to the lungs, then back to the heart again.

The heart is separated into a left half and a right half.

Blood keeps going round the body. E

D

A

Blood passes from one side of the heart to the other through tiny holes.

The heart pumps blood around the body.

C

Blood is made in the liver and gets used up in other parts of the body.

Blood can flow through veins in one direction only.

F

G

B

Developing ideas

It took many centuries for scientists to discover how the heart works and blood flows. Below and on the opposite page you can find out how some of their ideas were developed.

Galen was a Greek doctor who worked in Rome from about 150 to 200 AD. The books he wrote were used for another 1400 years. He dissected bodies and studied the heart: his view of the heart is shown in the diagram on the right.

Galen thought that blood was made in the liver and used up in other parts of the body, but he could not prove this. He discovered two different sorts of tube that had blood in: **arteries** had thicker walls and were a lighter colour than **veins**. He believed that blood went from one to the other through the **septum**.

2 What is the septum?
3 Why might Galen have thought that blood was made in the liver?

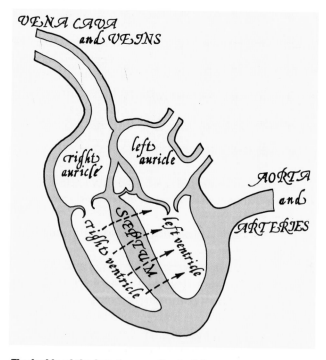

The inside of the heart according to Galen

In 1531, Galen's books were translated into French, and used by Andreas Vesalius in Padua, Italy. Vesalius did more dissections. He decided that he did not agree with all of Galen's ideas. Two extracts from his writings are on the right.

Realdo Columbo followed Vesalius as Professor of Medicine at Padua. He found that blood moved through arteries from the heart to the lungs, and through veins back to the heart. Fabricius, also at Padua, discovered that veins had valves in them. These only let blood flow in one direction.

4   Why did Vesalius think that Galen was wrong? Why do you think he did not say that Galen was wrong in the first edition of his book?
5   In what way did Columbo and Fabricius work differently from Vesalius?

William Harvey, an English doctor, studied at Padua from 1600 to1602, then continued his research in London. He published his findings in 1628. You can see some of his ideas on the right. Harvey made discoveries by doing experiments. He measured the amount of blood pumped by each heart beat. He also noticed that the ends of arteries and veins looked like tiny hairs. He thought that blood must pass between them, but could not see any connecting tubes and was unable to prove his theory. At about this time, other scientists were starting to use microscopes. In 1661, Marcello Malpighi, an Italian doctor, saw networks of microscopic blood tubes between arteries and veins.

6   Why do you think Harvey travelled to Padua to study?
7   How were Harvey's methods different from those of the earlier workers.
8   List the ideas which Harvey had about the heart and the blood. Which were based on experimental evidence?
9   How might Harvey have worked out how much blood was pumped in an hour?
10 Why was Harvey not able to find any connecting tubes between arteries and veins?
11 How did Malpighi's observations support Harvey's ideas?
12 List the scientists you have read about in this spread and the centuries in which they worked. Which of the statements A to E at the start would each scientist have believed to be correct at the time?
13 Which of the statements would a modern scientist think were incorrect?

First edition (1543)

❝ The septum of the heart is very dense. It has many pits on both sides but none seem to go through from the right to the left ventricle. We are, therefore, forced to wonder at the art of the Creator, that blood can pass through holes that cannot be seen. ❞

Second edition (1555)

❝ Not long ago, I would not have dared to differ from Galen's opinion. But the septum is as thick and dense as the rest of the heart. Therefore, I do not see how the smallest particle can pass from the right to the left through it. ❞

Extracts adapted from *Fabric of the Human Body*   by Vesalius

Here are some of Harvey's ideas:

'I think that blood circulates around the body. My experiments show that it leaves the heart through arteries and returns through veins. The heart works rather like a water pump. In one hour, more blood is pumped round the body than a person could possibly have produced from the food they ate.'

William Harvey

organ

Q 3.4 Heart of the matter

On the right, you can see what scientists now think the body's blood circulation system is like. Blood in the right side of the heart cannot mix with blood in the left. Each side of the heart operates as a separate pump, although the two must work together for the heart to be effective.

1 Which side of the heart pumps blood to the lungs?

2 Which side of the heart pumps blood round the rest of the body?

Any tube in the body which carries blood is called a **blood vessel**. The blood vessels in the diagram have been labelled A, B, C, D, O, P, Q and R:

3 In which of these blood vessels will the blood have most oxygen? Why?

4 In which of the blood vessels will the blood have most carbon dioxide? Why?

Inside the heart

On the opposite page, you can see a diagram of the heart. The heart has four chambers (spaces) filled with blood. Each time the heart beats, muscles in the walls of the chambers contract. As a result, blood is pumped from the chambers.

5 What is the name of the blood vessel bringing blood to the heart from the lungs?

6 What is the name of the blood vessel bringing blood to the heart from the rest of the body?

7 What is 'deoxygenated blood'? Which side of the heart contains deoxygenated blood?

8 Which side contains oxygenated blood?

9 Why do you think the muscle around the left ventricle is thicker than around the right?

10 Why do you think the ventricles have thicker walls than the atria ('atriums')?

11 What does the valve between atrium and ventricle do?

12 Rearrange the following to show the order in which blood flows through them (blood flows round and round, so it does not matter which one you start with):
heart body lungs heart

13 Now do this again. But this time, include the names of the blood vessels as well.

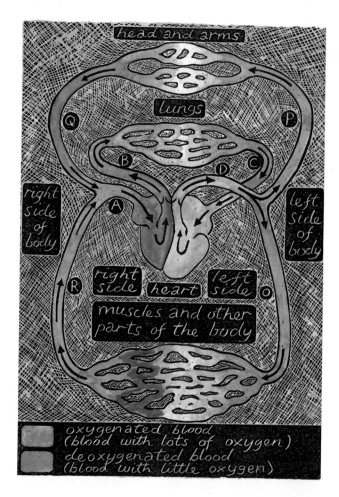

oxygenated blood (blood with lots of oxygen)
deoxygenated blood (blood with little oxygen)

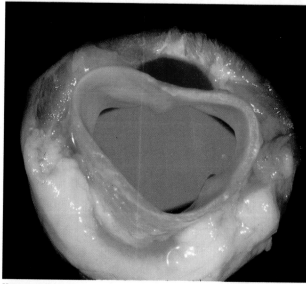

Heart valve, open

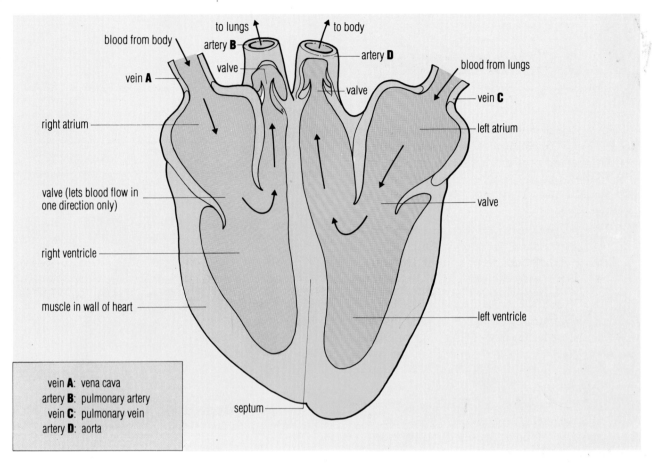

blood from body
to lungs
artery **B**
valve
to body
artery **D**
vein **A**
blood from lungs
valve
vein **C**
right atrium
left atrium
valve (lets blood flow in
one direction only)
valve
right ventricle
muscle in wall of heart
left ventricle
septum

vein **A**: vena cava
artery **B**: pulmonary artery
vein **C**: pulmonary vein
artery **D**: aorta

Arteries and veins

Arteries carry blood *away* from the heart. Veins carry blood *towards* the heart. Most arteries carry oxygenated blood, and most veins carry de-oxygenated blood. But there is an important exception in each case.

14 What artery carries deoxygenated blood?
15 What vein carries oxygenated blood?

Hole in the heart

Some babies are born with a 'hole in the heart'. The hole is in the septum, not in the outer wall. Often the hole is very small. It can usually be repaired by surgery.

16 If there was a hole in the outer wall what would happen to blood in the heart when the heart muscles contracted?
17 If there is a hole in the septum, how will this affect oxygenated and deoxygenated blood in the heart? Why will this be a problem to the person?
18 On the right, you can see a report by a young person with a hole in the heart. Write a reply, explaining what is happening to the person's blood and why he feels like he does. Use drawings to help your explanation.

Did you know?

If a hole in the heart is small, it may be years before anyone realizes that there is a problem. Asa Hartford was an international footballer. During a medical examination before a transfer to another club, he was found to have a hole in his heart. He carried on playing successfully.

" I didnt really want to go shopping because I had been feeling weak and tired. The shop assistant said I looked very pale. I had to stay on the ground floor because the lift was not working, and I felt out of breath as soon as I started walking upstairs. "

3.5 Heart surgery

In Britain, one person in four dies from heart disease. Smoking, lack of exercise, and eating food which is high in animal fat all increase the risk of heart disease. To tackle the problem, doctors sometimes have to perform complicated heart operations.

1 Some people think that it would be better to spend more money on preventing heart disease rather than on treating it. Do you agree or disagree with this idea? Explain your answer.

The heart is a muscle and needs oxygen just like any other muscle. So, as well as pumping blood round the body to all the other organs, the heart also needs its own supply of blood. It receives its blood through arteries in the wall of the heart, called the **coronary arteries**. In time, fat deposits may build up in these and cause a blockage.

2 Why does the heart muscle need its own supply of blood?

3 What do you think will happen if the supply of oxygen to the heart muscle is reduced
   a gradually?   **b** suddenly?

If a coronary artery becomes blocked, surgeons can **bypass** the blockage using a piece of vein taken from the patient's leg. The transferred piece is called a **graft**. You can see a graft in the diagram on the right.

4 What blood vessel is the graft attached to?

5 Is the blood in this vessel oxygenated or deoxygenated?

Heart valves

The valves in the heart can wear out, or fail due to disease. They can be replaced with plastic valves like the one in the photograph. Or valves from the heart of a dead donor can be used instead. However, the donor should be younger than sixty-five.

6 What is meant by a 'donor'?

7 Why do you think that valves from elderly donors are not normally suitable for heart surgery?

8 What do you think are the advantages and disadvantages of plastic valves compared to valves from donors?

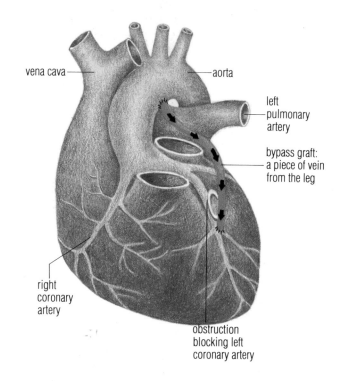

vena cava — aorta

left pulmonary artery

bypass graft: a piece of vein from the leg

right coronary artery

obstruction blocking left coronary artery

Bypassing a blocked coronary artery with a graft

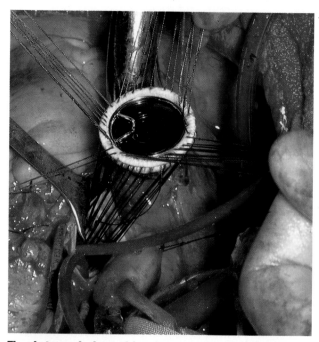

The photograph above shows heart surgery in progress. A damaged heart valve has been removed, and is being replaced by an artificial one.

Pacemakers

During each heart beat, the muscle of the wall of the heart contracts (squeezes up). Most muscles in the body need a signal from the brain telling them to contract. The signals are called **stimuli** and they pass along nerves. However, the stimuli that make the heart beat come from inside the wall of the heart itself. The part that sends them out is called the **pacemaker**.

9 Several things can affect the rate at which the heart beats. What examples can you think of?

Sometimes, the heart's own pacemaker may break down completely and not tell the heart muscle to contract. Or it may send out signals irregularly, or very slowly.

10 What effect do you think each of these faults would have on a patient?

11 What do you think the artificial pacemaker in the photograph does?

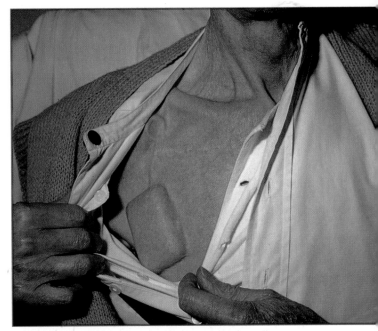

Artificial pacemaker under the skin of a patient

Heart transplants

For some heart patients, there is only one hope of survival: receiving a healthy heart from another person. This is called a **transplant**. The patient receiving the heart is the **recipient**. Usually, only people close to heart failure, with less than six months to live, are considered for a transplant. The donor is often an accident victim who is too seriously injured to survive but whose heart is undamaged. Permission must be given in advance by the donor or close relatives, and the donor's heart must match the recipient's body. The operation takes up to five hours. More than 50% of recipients gain an extra five years of life.

12 What do you think is meant by 'the donor's heart must match the recipient's body'?

13 During a transplant operation, blood must not flow to the heart and lungs. So the patient's blood must be oxygenated and pumped artificially. Why is it important that this is done?

14 The diagram on the right shows how the donor's heart is connected to the recipient's blood vessels. Name the parts being connected at the places labelled **1**, **2**, **3** and **4**.

Heart and lungs are often transplanted together. If this is done:

15 Which of the connections would not have to be made?

16 What other connections would have to be made?

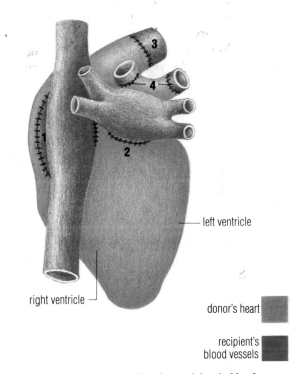

left ventricle

right ventricle

donor's heart

recipient's blood vessels

The donor's heart is connected to the recipient's blood vessels at the places labelled 1, 2, 3 and 4

Did you know?

The first heart transplant was carried out in 1967 in South Africa by Dr Christian Barnard. The patient, Louis Washansky, lived for 18 days. He died of pneumonia, not of a failure of the transplanted heart.

3.6 Digestion and the stomach

The food we eat is of little use in our bodies until it has been digested, and then absorbed by our blood. This happens in the **alimentary canal**. The alimentary canal is sometimes known by a shorter name: the **gut**.

1 Which of the following statements describes *digestion*?

    A small molecules of food passing from the alimentary canal into the bloodstream.

    B larger molecules of food being broken down into smaller ones.

2 Which of the above describes *absorption*?

3 List as many parts of the alimentary canal as you can, and say what each one does. The picture on the right may help you.

The chemicals that carry out digestion are called **enzymes**.

4 In what ways do enzymes change food?

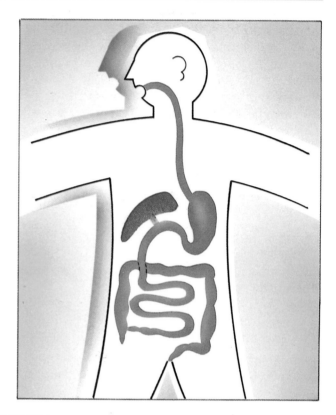

Investigating pepsin

Pepsin is a digestive enzyme produced in the stomach lining. Released from the lining, it pours onto food in the stomach.

Find out whether pepsin digests food better in acid or alkaline conditions.

You need
Cooked egg white in water, acid, alkalis, test tubes.

Useful information
- Pepsin is an enzyme that digests protein.
- Egg white is a good source of protein.
- Cooked egg white turns clear when digested.

What to do
- Set up the test tubes as shown on the right. Put the egg white into each tube first and mix the liquids together by shaking them gently.
- Leave the liquids to stand and observe them closely. Record what you see.
- What will the results of test tubes A and B tell you?
- Why are test tubes C, D, E and F each needed?
- Under what conditions did pepsin appear to work best?

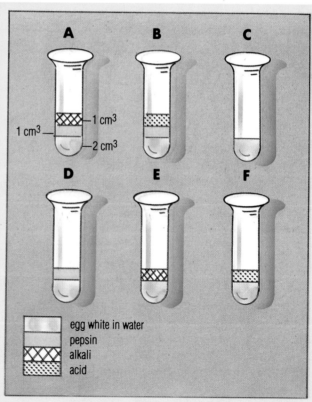

egg white in water
pepsin
alkali
acid

166

More investigations
- Find out the temperature at which pepsin works best.
- Find out whether pepsin digests starch. (Hint: starch is changed into glucose when it is digested. Can you test for starch and for glucose?)

Inside the stomach

In the stomach, pepsin is released from glands along with hydrochloric acid and thick mucus. The mixture is called **gastric juice**. The mucus helps to protect the stomach wall. Look at the diagram on the right.

5 Why do you think the stomach wall has layers of muscle in it?

6 Why is the stomach wall covered in pits?

7 Why do you think the stomach wall needs to be coated with mucus?

If acid and enzymes 'eat' into the stomach wall, the result is a stomach **ulcer**. This can be extremely painful. People with ulcers can be given medicines to protect the stomach lining.

8 Why do you think people with stomach ulcers are advised to include eggs and milk (both high in protein) in their diet, and to avoid spicy food?

Looking into indigestion

Indigestion may be caused if too much gastric juice is produced. This can happen if a person does not eat regularly, or eats their food too quickly.

9 Why would each of these things mean that there is too much gastric juice in the stomach?

Indigestion tablets or liquids are taken to ease the pain. They help neutralize the acid.

10 What type of chemical will neutralize acid?

- Carry out some laboratory tests on indigestion tablets to find out which is best at neutralizing acid. Produce a report on what you did and the results you found.
- Investigate some of the other factors which should be considered when selecting indigestion tablets.

Things to think about
- What effect will an indigestion tablet have on acid? How can you measure the effect?
- How will you make your tests fair?

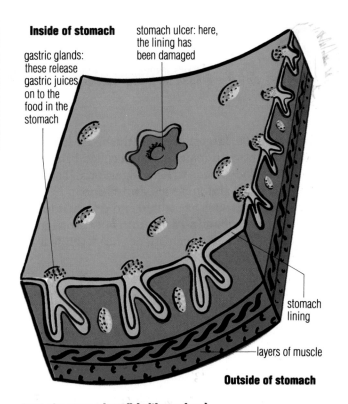

Inside of stomach

gastric glands: these release gastric juices on to the food in the stomach

stomach ulcer: here, the lining has been damaged

stomach lining

layers of muscle

Outside of stomach

Part of a stomach wall (with an ulcer)

3.7 The liver and kidneys

The liver is the largest organ in the body. It has many functions. It makes a liquid called **bile**, which the body needs to help digest fats. It stores some vitamins and minerals, and destroys harmful things such as alcohol and drugs. It turns chemicals called **amino acids** into new proteins, and converts those which are not needed into a substance called **urea**.

The diagram on the right shows the liver and the blood vessels connected to it. You may already know something about the liver from earlier work. If so, see if you can answer these questions:

1 Where does urea go?
2 What does blood in the hepatic portal vein carry to the liver?
3 What does the liver do to this material?
4 The liver is red in colour because of its large blood supply. Why does it need a large blood supply?
5 Where does the blood flowing through the aorta come from?

The liver uses a lot of energy to carry out its jobs, so it needs a good supply of oxygen. After passing through the liver, the blood has lost so much pressure that it has to return to the heart to be pumped to other parts of the body.

6 Through what two blood vessels does the liver receive oxygenated blood?
7 What two blood vessels will blood pass through to get back to the heart?
8 Where does this blood go next after passing through the heart?

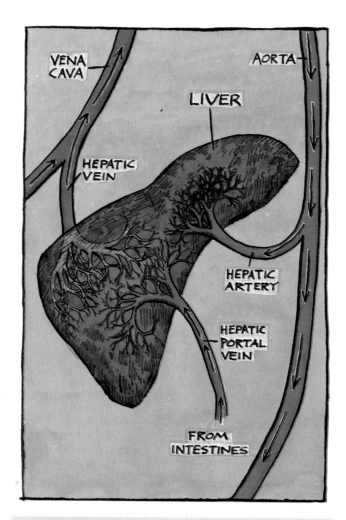

Hydrogen peroxide and the liver

Hydrogen peroxide is a waste product of many of the body's chemical reactions. It is very toxic (poisonous). To destroy it, the liver makes an enzyme called **catalase**.

The effect of the liver on hydrogen peroxide can be investigated in the laboratory. The photograph on the right shows what happens when a piece of liver (from a butcher) is put in hydrogen peroxide. Carry out similar investigations to see if you can find answers to some of the questions at the top of the next page.

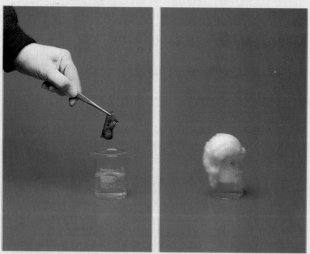

What happens when a piece of liver is put in hydrogen peroxide

Questions for investigation, based on the experiment shown in the photograph on the opposite page:

- How can you collect the gas given off?
- What gas is produced?
- How much gas is produced in a minute?
- When the bubbling stops, is it because the liver has stopped working or because all the hydrogen peroxide has been used up?
- What is the effect of using several small pieces of liver instead of one lump?
- What happens if the liver is boiled first?
- What happens if the hydrogen peroxide is at different temperatures?

Cleaning the blood

The kidneys are continuously 'cleaning' the blood. They remove many substances from the blood by filtering, then they put back those substances which the body still needs.

You can see a diagram of a kidney on the right. Blood flows into the kidney at high pressure. Water and other substances are forced from the blood, through thin membranes in the **Bowman's capsules**, where they drain into tiny **tubules**. However, substances which the body still needs are reabsorbed by the blood as they flow through the tubules. For example, almost all the water, glucose and sodium forced out of the blood is reabsorbed. Waste liquid flows on through the tubules. The tubules join up and take the liquid, called **urine**, to the bladder.

9 What job is done by the kidneys?
10 List, in order, starting with the renal artery, the structures (parts) a substance passes through if it is *not* reabsorbed by the blood.
11 Now list the structures a substance passes through if it is reabsorbed by the blood.

Dialysis machines

If a person's kidneys are not working properly, a **dialysis machine** may be used to help filter their blood. The patient may be attached to the machine for several hours, about three times a week.

12 Draw your own version of the picture on the right. Add arrows to show which way the blood is flowing.
13 Why must the blood be passed through the machine several times and not just once?
14 Why do you think it is not necessary for the person's blood to be filtered every day?

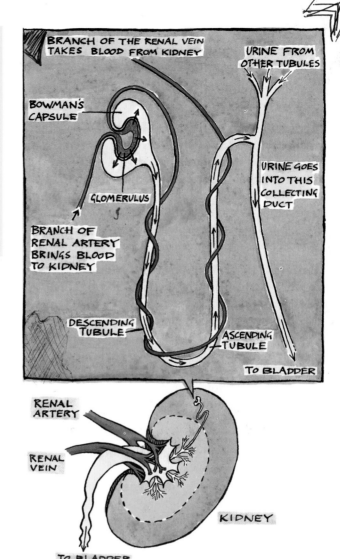

Inside a kidney. This diagram has been greatly simplified. A real kidney has about a million tiny tubules in it, with the same number of Bowman's capsules for filtering the blood.

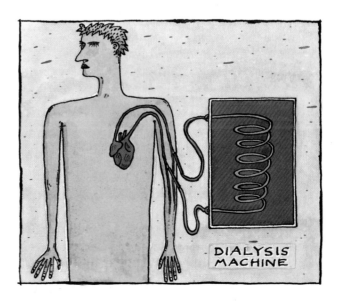

169

3.8 Bones, muscles and joints

There are about 200 bones in your body. Together, they form a **skeleton** which protects many of your organs. It also provides a framework for your muscles so that they can make movements. The bones are important in another way as well: they store minerals such as calcium and phosphorus.

1 What organs are protected by the skeleton? List your ideas.

Look at the diagram on the right. It shows the structure of the arm. The **tendons** and **ligaments** are strong bands of fibres.

2 Which of the following describes what ligaments do?
   A join muscles to bones
   B join bones to bones at a joint.
3 What do tendons do?
4 How would you describe a joint? (Think about its structure and the jobs it does.)
5 Try to find the tendons in your own arm. (Hint: muscles feel quite soft, tendons feel hard.)
6 Feel what happens to the length of the biceps and triceps muscles when you bend and then straighten an arm. You may need to use a friend's arm for this!

A muscle can only contract (shorten). It cannot stretch on its own. An opposite muscle must contract in order to stretch it. A pair of muscles working together in this way is called an **antagonistic** pair.

7 Use a dictionary to find the meaning of the word 'antagonistic' (or 'antagonize').
8 Look at the diagram of the arm. What happens to the triceps muscle if the biceps muscle contracts?

Inside the leg

Look at the diagram of the leg on the right.

9 How is the arrangement of the bones and muscles similar to that in the arm?
10 What happens to the leg if muscle B contracts?
11 Which muscle has to contract to get the leg back to its original position?
12 Which muscles move the foot up and down? Explain how they do this.

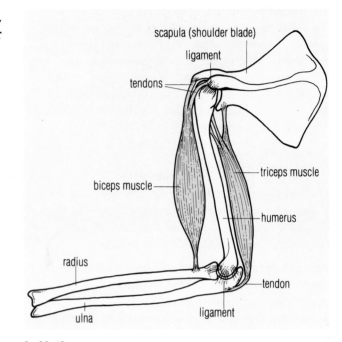

Inside the arm

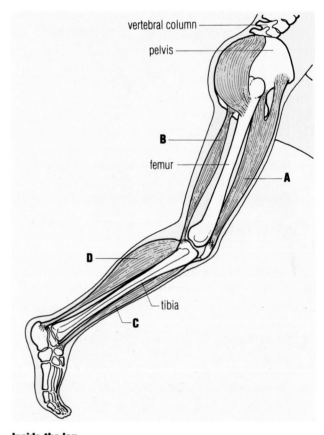

Inside the leg

170

Joints

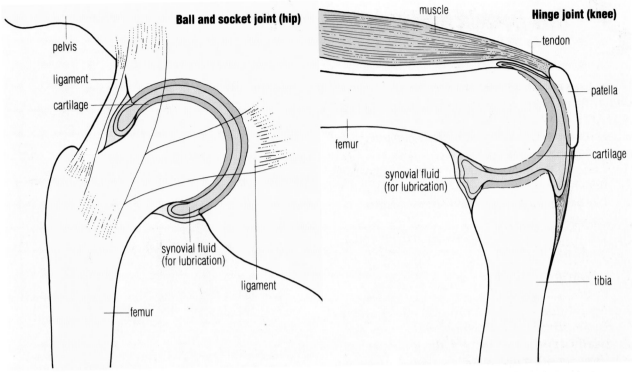

Ball and socket joint (hip)
- pelvis
- ligament
- cartilage
- synovial fluid (for lubrication)
- ligament
- femur

Hinge joint (knee)
- muscle
- tendon
- patella
- cartilage
- femur
- synovial fluid (for lubrication)
- tibia

Joints are places where two bones meet. Most joints bend so that the bones can move. In your hips and shoulders, the bones can move in all directions, like the gearstick in a car. But in your elbows and knees, the joints can only bend one way.

There are two main types of joint in your body. These are called the **hinge joint** and the **ball and socket joint**. The diagrams above show an example of each type.

13 Which type of joint do you think is found in each of these parts of the body:
  a elbow **b** shoulder **c** thumb
  d finger **e** toe ?

Problems with bones

As bones get older, they tend to get weaker and break more easily. In elderly people, the head (top) of the femur may become worn away, or it may not mend on its own after it is broken. If so, it may have to be replaced with an artificial one. People sometimes say that the person is being given an 'artificial hip' .

14 Do you think that 'artificial hip' is an accurate description? Explain your answer.

15 What properties do you think the material used for an artificial femur head should have?

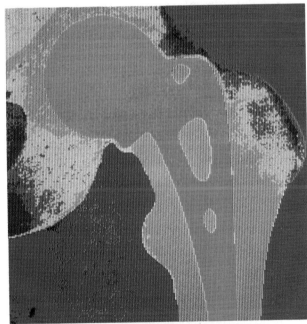

X-ray (in false colour) showing an artificial hip joint

Did you know?

Many elderly women suffer from weakened bones. This happens because calcium has been lost from the bones and not replaced. It can be caused by changes in the levels of female sex hormones which occur when a woman stops having periods.

3.9 Drugs and medicines

Drugs are substances which affect the way our bodies work. Some have good effects and some are harmful. All medicines contain drugs. However, not all drugs are medicines. Alcohol is a drug but not a medicine.

1 Can you think of any other examples of drugs which are not medicines? List your ideas.
2 List some good effects and some harmful effects of drugs.
3 What is the difference between a drug and a medicine?

Drug dependence

If people suffer unpleasant physical effects when they stop using a drug, doctors say that they are **physically dependent** on the drug. If people feel unhappy, tense or anxious when they stop using a drug, doctors say they are **emotionally dependent** on the drug. Sometimes, people can have both sorts of dependence.

4 What physical effects might someone suffer if they stopped taking a drug?

Barbiturates were once widely used as sleeping tablets, but they caused physical dependence. Look at the graph on this page.

5 What changes can you see in the numbers of sleeping tablets prescribed?
6 Why do you think scientists developed benzodiazepines (pronounced 'ben-zo-die-ay-zee-peens')?
7 When do you think doctors started to find that their patients were becoming dependent on the new sleeping tablets?

The people on the right are all users of drugs.

8 What drug does each person use?
9 Who is physically dependent on the drug? Who is emotionally dependent? Who may be both?
10 Which people believe that they are *not* dependent on a drug?
11 Whose health would be seriously harmed if they stopped taking their drugs?
12 Which drugs may have been prescribed by a doctor?
13 Some people have chosen to take drugs. What reasons do you think they might give?

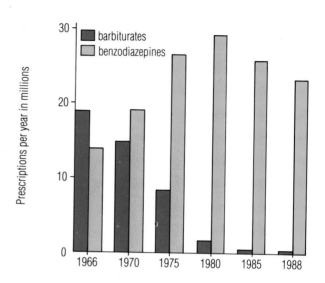

Sleeping tablets prescribed by doctors in Britain over a 12 year period.

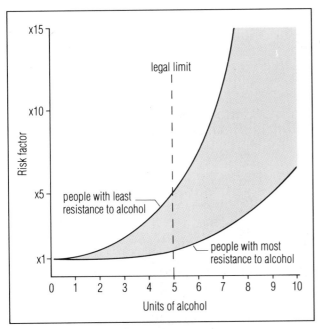

The risk factor tells you how many times greater the risk of an accident is than normal, when driving.
One unit of alcohol is about half a pint of beer, a glass of wine, or one measure of whisky.

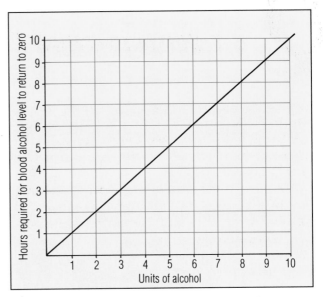

This graph shows how quickly alcohol is eliminated (removed) from the blood.

Alcohol

Alcohol starts to be absorbed into the blood a few minutes after the first drink. It takes much longer for all alcohol to be eliminated (removed) from the blood.

Use the graphs above to answer these questions.

14 Approximately how many units of alcohol can a person drink and be under the legal alcohol limit for driving?

15 How many units are eliminated from the blood every hour?

16 A person has drunk four pints of beer. How many units will there be in their blood?

17 This person has a high resistance to alcohol. How many times greater than normal is their risk of an accident?

18 How long will it be before their blood is free of alcohol?

19 Someone with a low resistance to alcohol is on the legal limit. How many times greater than normal is their risk of an accident?

20 Do these graphs support the argument that the legal level for alcohol in the blood should be much lower? Give your reasons.

21 Produce a poster or leaflet giving reasons why people should not drink and drive.

Did you know?

Alcohol plays a part in half of all the fatal road accidents in Britain.

Q 4.1 Getting better?

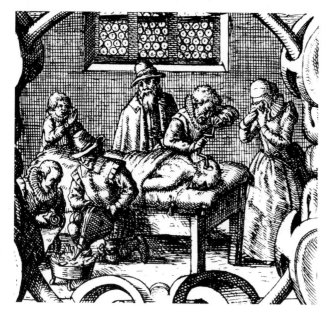

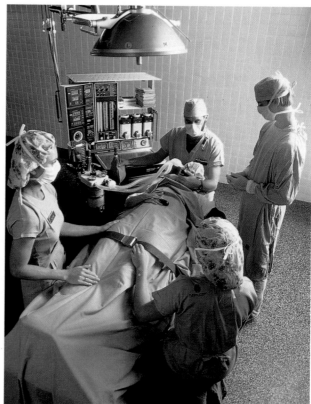

Most people spend some time in hospital during their lives. For some, it may only be a visit to an outpatients' department. Others may have to remain in hospital for longer periods.

1 Try to find out about the hospitals in your area. Here are some questions you could try to answer about them:
   • Do any specialize in treating certain types of illness?
   • Do any specialize in treating certain sorts of patients?
   • Which ones have accident and emergency departments? (People often call these 'casualty departments'.)

2 In your group, think of some more questions, then try to find the answers to them.

Changes in hospitals

Treatment in hospitals has changed a great deal over the years. Many changes have been due to the development of machines using advanced technology. However, the most important changes have happened because doctors have learnt much more about diseases and how they are spread.

3 Look at the pictures above. What differences can you see between the old operating theatre and the modern one?

4 What knowledge do you think modern doctors have which the doctors who worked in the old operating theatre would not have had?

5 How has their knowledge been used to make operating theatres safer places for patients?

One change in hospitals has been very slow: the different jobs done by men and women. Since early times, most doctors have been men. When medicine became more scientific in the 17th and 18th centuries, and proper training was given, women had even less chance of becoming doctors.

6 Why do you think that, even today, most doctors are men and most nurses are women?

The first woman doctor of modern times was Elizabeth Blackwell, an American teacher. She taught herself science, then paid for her course in medical school. She qualified as a doctor in 1849. In 1853 she set up a clinic for poor women and children.

7 Why do you think that the poor would be more likely to accept women doctors than the rich?

Did you know?

The first British woman doctor was Elizabeth Garrett. She qualified in Paris in 1870.

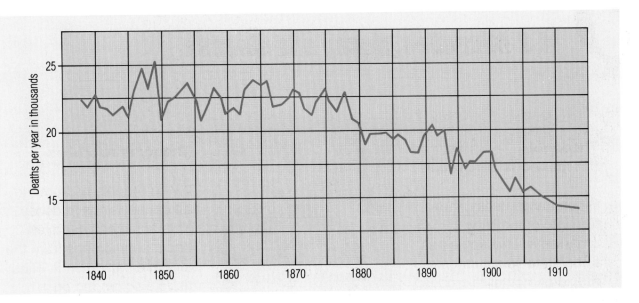

Living longer

The average length of time that people in a population live is called their **life expectancy**. In Britain today, people's life expectancy is longer than it has ever been. Some think that life expectancy tells you how healthy a population is. But others disagree.

8 Are people in a country with a long life expectancy necessarily more healthy than those in a country with a shorter life expectancy? Discuss this with your group and write down your ideas.

The graph above shows the death rate in England and Wales for the years between 1838 and 1914. On the right, there is some information about events between those years.

9 Which events would have helped reduce the death rate? (List the years.)

10 Does the graph give any evidence that these events did reduce the death rate? (Remember: changes may have taken a few years to have an effect.)

11 Copy the graph and mark on the events which you think reduced the death rate.

12 See if you can find out about other medical developments during this time.

13 What happened in 1914 that would have increased the death rate and made any more data misleading?

As you use this book and find out more about developments in the twentieth century, you may wish to keep a record of events that have helped to extend our life expectancy.

1840	An official enquiry recommends that a pure water supply should be provided and that drainage and refuse collection should be organized.
1847	Anaesthetics are used for the first time in surgical operations.
1860	A nursing school which trains nurses in the hygiene methods of Florence Nightingale is opened.
1861	Pasteur proves that germs cause decay and it seems likely that they cause diseases also.
1865	Antiseptics are used in operations for the first time.
1867	All male house owners are allowed to vote. Before, only the richer classes were allowed to vote.
1875	Parliament passes a Public Health Act which says that all Town Councils have to build effective sewers and water systems.
1887	Sixteen hospitals have nurses who have been trained in Florence Nightingale's methods.
1900	Most British towns have now built effective and hygienic sewer and water systems.
1901	Queen Victoria dies.
1906	Some children are able to have free meals at school.

4.2 Microbes, decay and disease

Theory of spontaneous generation

When things decay, they turn into other living organisms. This apple has turned into flies, maggots, mould and other microbes.

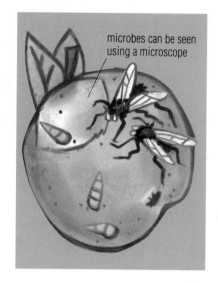

microbes can be seen using a microscope

Theory of microbes

Living organisms from the air cause things to decay. This apple has decayed because microbes from the air have settled on it. Flies have also landed on it. Flies lay eggs which hatch into maggots.

Above, you can see a picture of a decaying apple, together with two theories to describe the decay.

1 At one time, people thought that maggots and worms in decaying food grew out of the food itself. What was this theory called?
2 What are microbes?

In the early 19th century, some scientists suggested that microbes were the cause of the decay, and not the result. They thought that microbes might spread decay and possibly disease by floating through the air and settling on things.

3 Where do you think microbes come from?
4 How can microbes get into the air?

Pasteur's experiment

Louise Pasteur, a French chemist, was the first to show that the microbes which cause decay could be carried by air. He did so by performing an experiment like the one shown on the right. He partly filled the two flasks with broth (meat soup), sterilized the broth by boiling it, and then left the flasks to cool. Several days later, the broth in one of the flasks had gone bad, showing that microbes must have got into the flask from the air.

5 Why were the flasks and broth sterilized at the start of the experiment?
6 Why were microbes more likely to get into one flask than the other?

Pasteur published his results in 1861. Other scientists repeated his work. Some used different shaped flasks, but the results were always the same: if microbes could not get into the flask, the broth would not go bad.

7 Why is it important that scientists publish their results for others to read?

Did you know?

The process of **pasteurization** is named after Pasteur. See if you can find out how it is done and what effect it has.

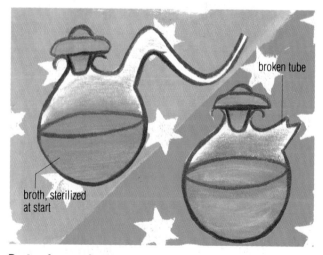

broken tube

broth, sterilized at start

Pasteur's experiment

Microbes and disease

Pasteur showed that some diseases of plants and animals were caused by microbes. Later, Robert Koch, a German doctor, showed that some diseases in humans were also caused by microbes. Microbes which cause disease are often known as **germs**.

Koch began his work in 1872. He found a way of staining microbes so they could be seen more easily under a microscope. In 1878, he identified the microbes that cause wounds to go septic (infected, and filled with pus).

8 If, as a scientist, you had identified the microbes in septic wounds, how would you try to prove that it was those microbes that made wounds go septic? Discuss your ideas with your group.

By 1900 Koch and his team had identified the microbes causing 21 diseases. Then Emil Behring, an assistant of Koch, found that some animals produced an **anti-toxin** in their blood to fight the toxin (poison) produced by microbes. He extracted the anti-toxin, and injected it into humans.

9 How would this help to cure the humans?

1861 Louis Pasteur publishes the results of his experiments on microbe theory.

1878 Rober Koch discovers the microbes that make wounds go septic.

1891 Emil Behring uses anti-toxins to cure a child of diptheria.

1909 Paul Ehrlich successfully treats syphilis using the first 'magic bullet', Salvarsan.

1928 Alexander Fleming discovers a new substance, penicillin, which can kill many germs.

1932 Gerhard Domagk uses a substance called a sulphonamide to cure his daughter's blood poisoning.

1941 Howard Florey's team extracts enough penicillin to show that it can be used to kill a variety of germs inside the body.

1943 Penicillin is first produced in large quantities; it starts to save many lives.

Stained glass windows in St Mary's Church, Paddington, showing Alexander Fleming at work in his laboratory. The laboratory was in a hospital close to the church.

Looking for magic bullets

Paul Ehrlich was one of Behring's students. He started to search for other substances which would work in the same way as natural anti-toxins. He said he was trying to 'shoot microbes with magic bullets'. It took him 10 years to find the first 'magic bullet', a substance called Salvarsan. It was the 606th substance his team had tried. The chart on the left gives more details about the development of 'magic bullets'.

10 Why do you think Ehrlich used the words 'magic bullets'?

11 What disease was Salvarsan used to treat?

12 Who first used a sulphonamide as a cure?

Penicillin is probably the most important 'magic bullet'. It was discovered by accident in1928, when Alexander Fleming noticed that a mould on a jelly-filled plate had killed the microbes next to it. Fleming was unable to purify the mould juice and extract much penicillin. However the problem was solved in 1941 by a team led by Howard Florey. Florey's team found that penicillin was effective against many serious infections, including pneumonia. But large amounts only became available when the British and US governments decided to support production.

13 Why, in 1941, do you think the British and US governments might have been especially keen to support the production of penicillin?

14 Look back at all the developments described in this spread. What do you notice about the rate of these developments?

4.3 Protecting against disease

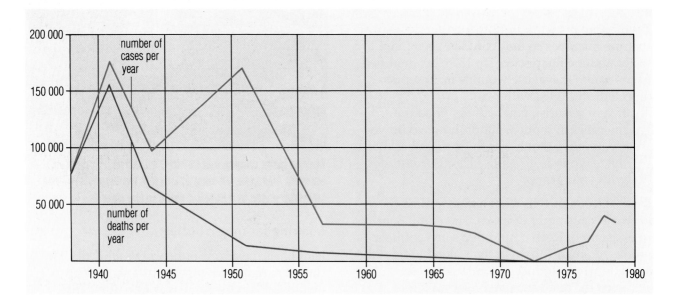

If a disease can spread from person to person, it is called an **infectious** disease. Whooping cough is one example. The graph above shows how many children caught whooping cough in Britain for each year between 1938 and 1978. It also shows how many children died from the disease.

1 How dangerous a disease was whooping cough in the late 1930s? How can you tell from the graph lines?
2 When did the death rate first start to fall? Why do you think this was?
3 When was the number of people suffering from the disease lowest?

Vaccination

For the past forty years or so, children have been **immunized** against certain diseases by putting substances called **vaccines** into their bodies. The process is called **vaccination**.

4 If you are 'immune' from a disease, what does this mean? See if you can find out what diseases you have been immunized against.
5 Look at the table on this page. Some of the figures in each column are the same. Why do you think this is?
6 Why do you think fewer children are immunized against measles than against diptheria, tetanus and polio?

Whooping cough: cases and deaths per year in Britain

Disease	% of children immunized in England and Wales				
	1973	1976	1977	1978	1979
diptheria	81	75	78	78	80
tetanus	81	75	78	78	80
polio	81	75	78	78	80
whooping cough	79	39	41	31	35
measles	54	47	50	48	51

A question of risk

In the 1970s, it became known that the whooping cough vaccine had caused brain damage in some children, though the percentage of children affected was extremely small.

7 What effect did this news have on the number of children being vaccinated?
8 How did this affect the number of children catching whooping cough?
9 Today, doctors still recommend that children should be vaccinated against whooping cough. What do you think their reasons are for giving this advice?

How vaccination was developed

If you have been vaccinated against a disease, you cannot normally catch it. You are immune.

The ancient Chinese knew that it was unusual to catch some diseases twice. They tried using this idea to protect themselves against a serious and normally fatal disease called smallpox. They took liquid pus from sores on someone suffering from a mild form of smallpox. Then they scratched the pus into a healthy person.

10 What effect did they hope this would have?

Edward Jenner was a family doctor who worked in Gloucestershire in the 1790s. He knew that some of the local people seemed to be immune to smallpox. He noticed that these were the same people who had previously caught cowpox, a much milder disease transmitted from cows. He thought that this might have given them protection against smallpox.

To test his idea, Jenner infected an eight year old boy, James Phipps, with cowpox. You can see how he did this on the right. Later, he twice attempted to infect the boy with smallpox using pus taken from a smallpox victim. The boy did not catch the disease. Jenner repeated his experiment with 22 other people. None caught smallpox. Jenner had successfully used cowpox pus as a vaccine for smallpox. Since Jenner's time, vaccines have been developed for many other diseases.

11 How did Jenner infect James Phipps with cowpox?

12 Why did Jenner want him to catch cowpox?

13 What would have happened to James Phipps if Jenner's idea had been wrong?

14 Do you think Jenner's experiments would be acceptable today? Discuss your ideas with your group.

14 May, 1796: Edward Jenner is about to use a needle with pus on to make cuts in the arm of eight-year-old James Phipps. He has taken the pus from sores on the hand of Sarah Nelmes, a dairymaid suffering from cowpox.

How vaccination works

When you catch a disease, your body produces antibodies to fight it. Some of these stay in your blood, ready to fight the disease if it enters your body again. Vaccines contain dead or very weak microbes. They do not make you ill. But they do make your body produce antibodies to the disease.

15 What effect will these antibodies have if you come into contact with the disease?

16 Look at the graphs below. Describe in words what they show.

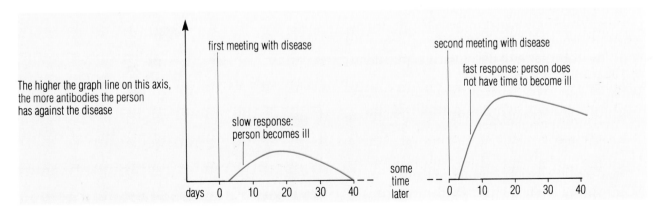

The higher the graph line on this axis, the more antibodies the person has against the disease

first meeting with disease

slow response: person becomes ill

days 0 10 20 30 40

some time later

second meeting with disease

fast response: person does not have time to become ill

0 10 20 30 40

4.4 Winning the battle?

The fight against disease continues. But some microbes seem to be fighting back.

1 Which *three* events in the battle against disease do you think have been the most important? Discuss your ideas.

The battle against malaria

Malaria is a disease which makes people sweat and shiver uncontrollably. In tropical countries, it kills millions every year. The disease is common near swampy areas where mosquitoes breed. In the 1880s, scientists found that the blood of malaria victims contains tiny, living organisms. In 1898, Ronald Ross, a doctor working in India, found that these organisms spent part of their life cycle in the stomachs of one type of mosquito.

2 How do you think malaria might be spread?
3 Why might draining swamps help solve the problem?
4 What other things could be done to help solve the problem?

DDT is an insecticide. Sprayed on swamps, it kills the mosquitoes. The graph on this page shows what happened to the number of malaria cases in India after DDT spraying started there.

5 When DDT spraying started, what was the effect on the number of cases of malaria?
6 For how long did DDT keep malaria under control?
7 When did DDT spraying stop being effective?
8 What happened to the number of malaria cases after this?

The diagram on the right shows how a population of living organisms can be affected by repeated spraying of a harmful chemical.

9 Why might some of the original population be resistant to the spray?
10 Why does the number of resistant organisms keep increasing from one generation to the next? What would Charles Darwin have called this?
11 Why do you think DDT spraying became less and less effective against mosquitoes?
12 See if you can find out any other reasons why DDT is not widely used any more?

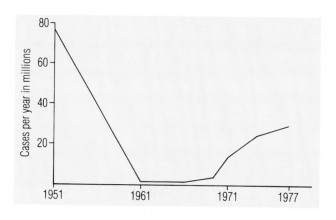

Cases of malaria in India, 1951 to 1977

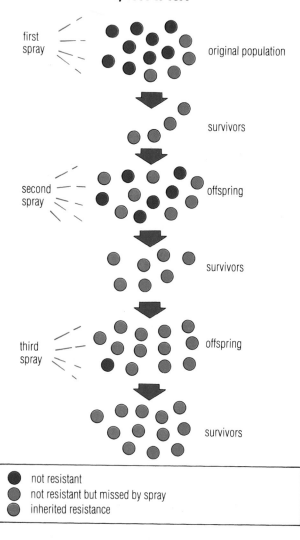

first spray — original population

survivors

second spray — offspring

survivors

third spray — offspring

survivors

● not resistant
● not resistant but missed by spray
● inherited resistance

How a population of organisms can become more and more resistant to a chemical spray

Germs fighting back

Like other living organisms, many germs breed. As a result, some have developed a resistance to the antiseptics and drugs used against them. Here is one example of how it can happen:

In the 1960s, American soldiers in Vietnam who caught syphilis were treated with penicillin. But penicillin was also given to healthy soldiers in case they caught the disease. As a result, those few syphilis germs with a gene which made them resistant to penicillin started to thrive and increase in number.

13 Why did penicillin become less and less effective against syphilis?

14 Chlorhexidene is an antiseptic which is widely used in hospitals. Use your own words and drawings to explain how some germs have become much more resistant to chlorhexidene than they used to be.

Transplant problems

When a patient receives a transplanted organ, it must be a good match for the recipient's body. If not, the body will produce antibodies to attack the 'foreign' organ. Transplanted organs are not usually an exact match, so the recipient's ability to produce antibodies must be reduced. For this, the recipient must be given injections which will destroy the white blood cells, called **lymphocytes**, which produce the antibodies. The injections contain the liquid part of blood (called **plasma**) taken from a horse. The diagram on the right shows how this special plasma is prepared.

15 Why does the horse produce antibodies to the white blood cells?

16 Why must all blood cells be removed from the horse's blood before the remaining plasma can be injected into the patient's blood?

17 How will the antibodies from the horse's plasma affect the patient's blood cells?

18 Why are transplant patients likely to suffer from common illnesses that might not harm other patients?

Hospital headlines

Hospitals have very high standards of hygiene, but problems like those in the newspaper headlines on the right can still occur.

19 Write an article describing the problems a hospital faces in controlling infections, and the steps that can be taken to overcome them.

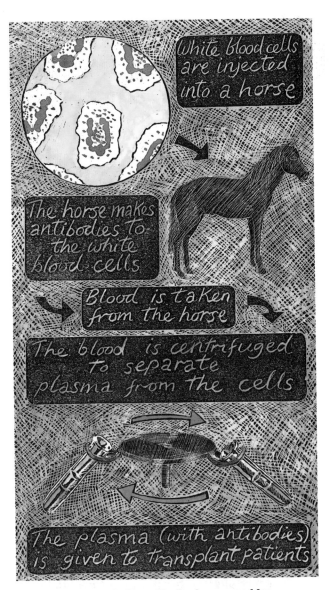

How plasma with suitable antibodies is prepared for transplant patients

Q 4.5 Micobes helpful and harmful

There are millions of microbes in your guts. Most are essential: they help digest your food or stop more harmful microbes from growing. Microbes also enter your digestive system whenever you eat or drink. Most of these are harmless, but some can be very dangerous.

Read the article on the right:

1 What two types of food-poisoning microbe does the article say are on the increase?
2 What reasons are given for the increase?
3 Why might the actual figures for salmonella poisoning be much higher than those found in the survey?
4 Why do you think the starting date for each graph is different?
5 What do you think is meant by 'cook-chilled foods'?
6 Why might microwave cooking be less effective than traditional cooking at killing microbes?
7 Do you think it is accurate to say that microbes have 'learnt to survive' in modern-day foods? Explain your answer.

Treating sewage

Sewage from toilets must be made safe, otherwise harmful microbes in human faeces might get into the water supply and infect thousands of people. The diagram at the top of the next page shows what happens at a sewage treatment works.

Beaten by Bugs

Scientists have found startling evidence to suggest that, for the past 40 years, Britain has been slowly losing the 'battle of the bugs'. The bugs in question are the microbes responsible for food poisoning. While some have been fought successfully, the statistics reveal that cases of salmonella and listeria poisoning have been increasing more or less continuously since 1950. Worse still, scientists think that, because of unreported cases, the actual figures of salmonella poisoning could be between 10 and 100 time higher than those in their survey.

The problem with food-poisoning microbes is that they have learned to survive among the modern methods used for food preparation. Some are unaffected by freezing. Others can survive temperatures as high as 350 °C. Storing chilled foods for increased lengths of time has helped new varieties to develop and multiply. Listeria hides in many of the cook-chilled foods we eat. It has killed very young children and affected the embryos of pregnant women.

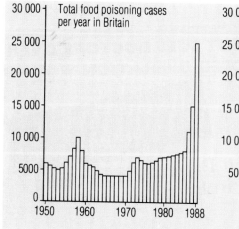

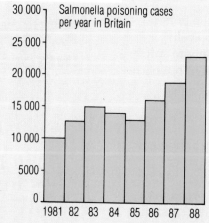

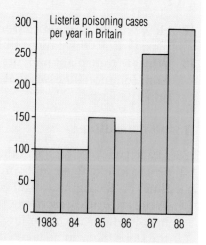

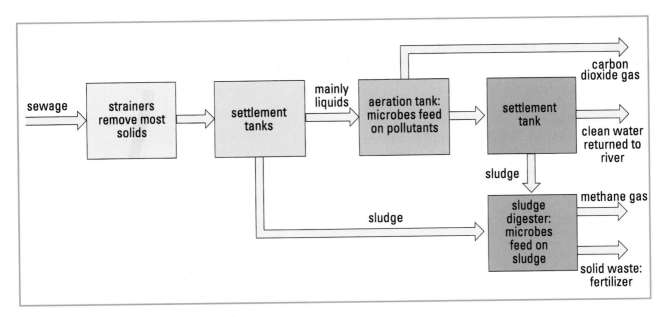

What happens at a sewage treatment works

Microbes help in the process of sewage treatment.

8 At what two stages are microbes important?
9 What two gases do the microbes produce?
10 Why does the action of microbes reduce the volume of waste produced?

Fit for the taps?

Harmful microbes must be removed before drinking water can be piped to your home. The water goes through two filter beds. It is also treated with chlorine and with aluminium sulphate.

11 Do you know why each chemical is used?

Investigate a model filter bed like the one shown on the right. Find the answer to one of the following questions (more if you have time):

- Does the size of the gravel make a difference to how well the filter bed works?
- Does it matter whether the large gravel is at the bottom or the top?
- Are long, narrow filters more effective than short, wide ones?
- What effect does aluminium sulphate have if added before or after filtering?
- Does the filter remove microbes from the water?

You need
Muddy water, washed sand and gravel of different sizes, plastic bottles of different sizes, aluminium sulphate, items chosen by you.

Safety: you must not drink the filtered water.

Did you know?

Even before the Romans, the Indians built aqueducts to supply water to their cities, and sewers to carry away waste. In Britain, it was not until 1875 that, by law, town councils had to build effective sewers. Until this time, water from raw sewage could find its way back into the drinking water supply.

4.6 Searching for success

The article on the right tells the final chapter in the story of scientists' successful fight against smallpox. However, in the fight against some other diseases, there is much further to go.

1 Smallpox has been 'eradicated'. What does this mean?

2 When was the last natural case of smallpox?

3 Why, after this case, do you think that samples of smallpox microbes were still being kept in a laboratory?

4 What other diseases have you heard of that used to kill many people but are rare today?

5 What scientific developments made it possible to reduce the effects of these diseases?

6 What diseases have you heard of that are still difficult or impossible to cure today?

The fight against smallpox and other diseases began many years ago. Some of the stories have been told in earlier pages.

7 Make a flow chart to summarize the fight against the diseases described. Your chart should include any important discoveries, the people who made them, and the approximate dates.

The fight to eradicate (wipe out) smallpox was made easier because the microbe that caused it could only survive in people. There was no other animal that it could 'hide' in.

8 What disease was greatly reduced when the mosquitoes that carry it were killed?

Cancer

Cancer is not a single disease, but a whole group of diseases. Unlike smallpox, AIDS and many other diseases, it is not infectious. At one time, few people used to recover from cancer. Today, many types of cancer can be treated successfully.

9 If a disease is 'infectious', what does this mean?

10 Is cancer infectious?

With cancer, something goes wrong with the mechanism that controls cell division. The diagrams at the top of the next page show what effect this can have.

World declared free of smallpox

The world is officially free of smallpox. The news was first given in a statement from the World Health Assembly in Geneva. In 1977, 3229 cases were reported, in Somalia. But since October 26 of that year, no further cases have come to light. The one exception was a small outbreak in 1978 due to an accident in a laboratory in the United Kingdom.

After the last reported case of smallpox, officials considered that a two year wait was necessary before they could declare that the disease had been eradicated. The eradication programme, started in 1967, cost nearly 140 million pounds. However, much more than this will be saved by not having to vaccinate people against the disease. In 1967, smallpox caused about 2 million deaths.

Smallpox is thought to have emerged around 10,000 BC. The mummy of Rameses V, dating from 1160 BC, shows evidence of a smallpox rash.

This man is increasing his risk of one type of cancer. Do you know which type?

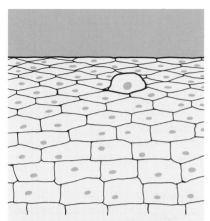

In the body, cell division is necessary for normal growth and repair. With most cells, the process is under control.

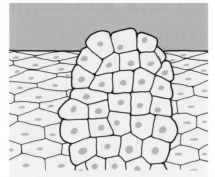

Occasionally, a cell may divide in an uncontrolled way. It forms a group of abnormal cells called a **primary growth**. These cancer cells take up more and more room. They may invade nearby parts of the body and stop them working properly.

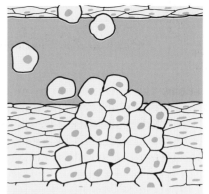

The cancer cells may break away and travel in the blood to other parts of the body. Here, they may settle and continue to divide rapidly, forming **secondary growths**. These may prevent other organs fron working properly.

Look at the diagrams above. They show how cancer cells can develop and spread.

11 What name is given to the type of cell division described in the first diagram?

12 What is a primary growth?

13 Why does a primary growth get bigger slowly at first, but then much more quickly?

14 What is a secondary growth?

Scientists know that some substances can cause cancer if they get into the body. Substances that cause cancer are called **carcinogens**.

15 List all the substances and other things you have heard of that may increase a person's chance of getting cancer.

The overall success rate in treating cancer is about 40%. The figure is much higher in patients where cancer has been found early.

16 Why do you think people have a much better chance of recovery if cancer is found and treated early?

Large doses of gamma or X-rays will kill cells. So they can be used to kill cancer cells. But radiation treatment like this can reduce a patient's resistance to disease.

17 In treating cancer, why must the radiation be carefully focused on the affected area?

18 Why might radiation treatment reduce a patient's resistance to disease?

AIDS

AIDS is affecting virtually every country in the world. In some populations, there are so many sufferers that doctors say there is an epidemic. Many people think that only homosexuals can catch AIDS, but this is not true.

Information about AIDS

- AIDS stands for:
  Acquired Immune Deficiency Syndrome

- AIDS is caused by a virus (a type of microbe) known as HIV (Human Immunodeficiency Virus).

- Not all people who are infected with HIV show symptoms of AIDS, but it is likely that they will get all AIDS eventually.

- HIV attacks the white blood cells which make antibodies. This means that AIDS sufferers lose their defence against even mild diseases, including some they were previously immune to.

- Three-quarters of AIDS patients die of pneumonia of the lungs.

- AIDS is infectious, but it can be transmitted in three ways only:
  1 By sexual contact
  2 By blood to blood contact
  3 From an infected mother to her unborn child.

- It is estimated that by the year 2000, 15 to 20 million people will have been infected by HIV.

- At present, there is no known cure for AIDS.

- A drug called AZT seems to delay the development of the disease by slowing down damage to the patient's white blood cells.

Look at the information about AIDS above.

19 Why do you think that AIDS is still spreading?

20 Why are AIDS patients likely to suffer badly from illnesses that would not harm other people?

Words and meanings

Alleles Genes which occupy matching positions along a pair of chromosomes and carry codes for the same characteristic. **Homozygous** alleles are the same. **Heterozygous** alleles have codes for opposite features.

Amplitude For a wave which can be drawn on paper, this is the height from the centre line to the top of a peak (or to the bottom of a trough).

Anode In an X-ray tube or a TV tube, this is the electrode which collects electrons.

Antibodies Substances made by the body to attack **antigens** (chemicals on the surface of microbes or other 'foreign' substances which invade the body).

Artery A blood vessel (tube) carrying blood *away* from the heart (see also **Vein**).

Asteroids Thousands of minor planets orbiting the Sun, mainly between the orbits of Mars and Jupiter. The largest, Ceres, is about a third the diameter of our Moon.

Capillaries Very narrow, thin-walled blood tubes linking arteries to veins.

Cathode In an X-ray tube or a TV tube, this is the electrode which emits electrons.

Chromosomes Structures within the nucleus of a cell which contain genes. Most chromosomes occur in pairs which match in size and shape. Pairs like this are called **homologous** pairs.

Core Central zone of the Earth, consisting mainly of hot, molten (liquid) iron. The **outer core** is liquid, but the **inner core** is kept solid by the extremely high pressure.

Crust The thin, outer layer of the Earth. The continents are mainly made of granite-like **continental crust**. Between these is the much thinner, basalt-based **oceanic crust**.

Depressions Weather systems where the air pressure is lower than normal and, north of the equator, the winds circulate anticlockwise. They are normally associated with wet or changeable weather.

Diffraction The spreading which occurs when waves (for example, light waves and sound waves) pass through narrow gaps or around obstacles.

Dispersion The splitting of white light into its different colours by, for example, a prism.

DNA (Deoxyribose nucleic acid) Substance in cells which carries the genetic code. Each chromosome has a long, coiled-up molecule of DNA running through it. The molecule is made from millions of tiny pieces of chemicals, including four **organic bases** (adenine, cytosine, guanine and thymine). The genetic code depends on the sequence of these bases.

Electrodes Plates used for emitting or collecting electrons in X-ray tubes, TV tubes or similar (see also **Anode** and **Cathode**).

Electromagnetic waves A family of waves whose members are (from longest wavelength to the shortest): radio waves, microwaves, infrared, visible light, ultraviolet, X-rays, gamma rays. The full range of waves is known as the **electromagnetic spectrum**.

Electrons Tiny particles which come from atoms and carry a negative (-) electric charge. The 'electricity' in a circuit is a flow of electrons.

Enzymes Substances made by the body to help vital chemical reactions, usually by speeding them up.

Erosion The wearing away of the surface of rock or other material. Weathering is one cause of erosion.

Fault Break between two masses of rock where one has moved relative to the other.

Focal length For a convex lens, the distance from the lens to the point of focus when the lens is receiving parallel rays of light.

Folds Bends in layers of rock. Peaks in folds are called **anticlines**. Troughs called are **synclines**.

Frequency The number of waves produced or sent out every second. If there is one wave per second, the frequency is 1 **hertz** (**Hz**).

Front Boundary between a mass of warm air and a mass of cold air. If a **warm front** passes, then cold air is followed by warm air. If a **cold front** passes, then warm air is followed by cold air.

Gametes Sex cells. In humans, **sperms** are the male gametes and **ova** ('ovums') are the female gametes. In plants the gametes are contained within the **pollen** grains (male) and **ovules** (female).

Gene One part of the chemical code in a chromosome. It carries coded information about one characteristic. Genes for a particular characteristic operate in pairs. If one gene masks the other, one is **dominant** and the other is **recessive**. If neither is dominant or recessive, the genes are **co-dominant**.

Genetics The study of inherited characteristics.

Genotype The set of genes which an organism has for a particular characteristic (see also **Phenotype**).

Igneous rocks Rocks formed from hot, molten (liquid) **magma** which has cooled and solidified.

Interference The reinforcing or cancelling out which can occur when two sets of similar waves pass through the same space. If the waves cancel, this is called **destructive interference**. If they reinforce each other, this is **constructive intereference**.

Intrusion A block of igneous rock which, as molten (liquid) magma, was forced between existing rocks before cooling and solidifying to form a band, dome or other shape.

Isobars Lines on weather maps through points where the air pressure is the same.

Kilowatt hour (kW h) Unit of energy used on domestic electricity meters. It is the energy delivered if an appliance with a power of 1 kilowatt (kW) is used for one hour.

Logic gates Electronic switches whose outputs are controlled by applying small voltages to their inputs.

Longitudinal waves Waves in which the vibrations are in the same line as the direction of travel (i.e backwards-and-forwards vibrations).

Magma Hot, molten (liquid) material in the Earth. When cooled, it forms **igneous rock**.

Mantle The thick layer of the Earth between the **crust** and the **core**. Made of **igneous** material, it is mainly solid, though some parts are liquid.

Meiosis Type of cell division in which **gametes** (sex cells) are formed. It happens in the organs of reproduction. Cells formed by meiosis only have half the number of chromosomes of the parent cell.

Metamorphic rocks Rocks formed when existing rocks are changed by the action of heat or pressure or both.

Microbes Microcopic organisms such as **bacteria**. **Viruses** and some **fungi** are also called microbes. Any microbes which cause disease are known as **germs**.

Mitosis Type of cell division which produces cells with the same number of chromosomes as the parent cell. In the body, all new cells needed for growth and repair are produced by mitosis.

Natural selection The process by which organisms slowly become **adapted** (suited) to their environment. Organisms within a group have slightly different features. Some features give an advantage in the struggle for survival. The survivors breed, so their features are passed on to their offspring.

Nebulae Large clouds of gas and dust in space. Stars and their planets form from the material within them.

Phenotype The physical appearance of a particular characteristic, as distinct from the genetic information for that characteristic (see also **Genotype**).

Plate tectonics The theory that the Earth's outer layer consists of large sections called **plates** which drift very slowly on the lower **mantle** beneath them.

Pollination The transfer of pollen grains from anthers to stigma in a plant. In **self-pollination**, the pollen comes from the same plant. In **cross-pollination**, it comes from a different plant of the same species.

Potentiometer A variable resistor connected so that it passes on a fraction of the supply voltage across it. The fraction can be varied by moving a control knob.

Principal focus For a convex lens, the point where rays focus when the lens is receiving parallel rays of light.

Refraction The bending which occurs when waves cross into a region where their speed is reduced. Light waves are refracted when they pass from air into glass or water.

Rock cycle The continuous cycle in which rock fragments are eroded, transported, deposited, and then re-used in the formation of new rocks.

Sedimentary rocks Rocks formed from layers of sediment. The sediment may consist of fragments of other rocks which have been carried by water, wind, ice or gravity.

Seismic waves Shock waves (earthquake waves) which travel through the Earth or over its surface from the site of an earthquake. There are three types, known as P, S and L waves.

Solar System The Sun and its planets, and all other natural objects (comets for example) in orbit around the Sun.

Spectrum The range of colours produced when white light is split into its different wavelengths, by a prism for example. On a wider scale, it can also mean the full range of electromagnetic waves.

Sunspots Patches on surface of the Sun where the temperature is lower than normal.

Thermionic emission The release of electrons from a material because of heating. For example, electrons being given off by a hot cathode in an X-ray tube or TV tube.

Transverse waves Waves in which the vibrations are at right angles to the direction of travel (e.g. up-and-down vibrations).

Ultrasound Sound whose frequency is above the range of human hearing.

Vaccine A substance put into the body to make it produce antibodies to a particular germ. Often, the vaccine is a mild or 'dead' version of the germ. The antibodies give the person protection against the real disease.

Vein A blood vessel (tube) carrying blood *towards* the heart (see also **Artery**).

Wavelength For a wave which can be drawn on paper, this is is the distance from one peak to the next (or from one trough to the next).

Weathering Process in which the surface of rock or other material is weakened by the action of the weather. Dissolving by the acid in rainwater is an example of **chemical weathering**. Frost damage is an example of **physical weathering**.

Index

Acknowledgements

The illustrations are by:

Harriet Dell, Nick Duffy, Clive Goodyer, Jean Hands, Nick Hawken, Helen Marsden, Hilary McManus, Patricia Moffett, Mark Rogerson, Mike Sharp, Ursula Sieger, Julie Tolliday, Russell Walker, Jim Wells and Galina Zolfaghari.

The publishers would like to thank the following for supplying photographs:

Heather Angel/Biophotos p 157 (bottom); Ardea p 84; Argos p 107; Associated Press p 75; J Allen Cash pp 17, 18 (bottom right), 21 (left), 130 (centre and right), 137, 144 (bottom), 157 (left); John Cleare/Mountain Camera p 26; Bruce Coleman Photographic Library p 146; Mary Evans Picture Library pp 138, 161, 174; Susan Griggs Photographic Library p 94; John Hopkins p 48; Landform Slides p 21; P Moffett p 130 (top); Oxford Scientific Films pp 145, 149 (all), 155 (all); Photo Library International pp 55 (left), 63 (top), 67, 68; Rex/Sipa pp 130 (left), 144; Michael Roberts p 144 (centre); Science Photo Library pp 24, 38, 52, 54 (right), 55 (right), 57 (right), 58 (left), 59 (top), 61, 63 (bottom), 65, 85, 87, 123, 127, 162, 164, 165, 171, 174, 177; Telegraph Colour Library p 59 (bottom); Tony Waltham pp 14 (all), 17, 22, 23, 25, 27, 28, 29, 32, 39, 69; Zefa Photographic Library pp 46, 86, 93, 125 (top & right), 157 (centre right).

Additional photography by Peter Gould, Chris Honeywell, Chris Moore. Special thanks to Mic Morgan, Oxfordshire Health Unit.